CW00350611

I Heard Every Word - Hypnotherapy Explained

David Lesser

By the same author:

THE BOOK OF HYPNOSIS
ISBN 0 9510875 25

First Published in Paperback 1985
Reprinted 1986
First Hardback Edition 1988
Reprinted 1991

Designed, Typeset and Printed in England by
Aston University

Published by
Curative Hypnotherapy Examination Committee
8 Balaclava Road, Kings Heath, Birmingham B14 7SG

ISBN 0 9510875 1 7

Contents

Foreword

I dumped the two suitcases in the hall and went through to the kitchen. I started going through the small mountain of bills that always seem to arrive when one is on holiday for just a couple of weeks. One of my daughters made a coffee while I went through the post and fifteen minutes later I returned to the hall to take the suitcases upstairs.

My mind was full of the bills and of returning to work as I bent down and grasped the handles. I straightened up and nearly fell on my back - the cases appeared to be weightless. My wife had already emptied them!

I began to think: the cases had been heavy, but not so heavy that they needed a tremendous effort to lift. I had not even thought about their weight so why had I put so much effort into lifting them that I almost lost my balance?

I had thought about taking them upstairs, but the effort I had put into lifting them was automatic. My brain had automatically allowed for the weight of the cases not knowing they had been emptied. My muscles had reacted without conscious thought and for the first time I started to really think about the muscles in my body.

I had been doing professional massage for years and was aware of basic anatomy and physiology. I knew about voluntary and involuntary muscles, but I had taken the text books as the whole truth and had not looked farther than the written word. Now I started to use my mind and realised that there is no muscle in the whole body which is under the direct control of the conscious mind; all muscles are operated by subconscious processes. The conscious mind may make a decision to act physically but it has to use subconscious mechanisms to actually carry out the action.

When teaching massage to my students I had always stressed that, although relaxation massage (not remedial) was a purely physical treatment, its biggest effect is on the mind. I put these thoughts on muscles together with some of the comments made by various ladies I had massaged: " My mind leaves my body", "It's like being hypnotised", "I just floated". The interrelation of the mind and body fascinated me and when some of my regular massage clients volunteered to act as guinea pigs, I started to experiment.

I cannot thank these ladies enough. Without their help I would not have taken up what is even more rewarding work than massage — Hypnotherapy - which must be the richest in job-satisfaction that anyone can imagine. Getting rid of the depression that someone has suffered for fifteen years, disposing of the migraine that has incapacitated a person for two or three days every week since teenage, allowing a so-called 'frigid' woman to enjoy sex or letting a child run and enjoy games without asthma, is a pleasure that not many people have. It has taken me years of learning, research and experimentation, not simply to find out how to induce hypnosis in others, not just to discover ways of alleviating their symptoms, but to learn ways of uncovering the cause of their problem then putting that cause right so their trouble cannot come back again. The fact that there is a permanent CURE makes the work really worthwhile.

I hope this book will give some insight into hypnosis and the correct use of hypnotherapy, that it will give an idea of the vast number of problems can be cured, of the methods used and will allay some of the apprehension that many people feel about this treatment. In particular I hope that the numerous people who have had 'hypnotic treatment' which was just an attempt to reduce their symptoms, will not give up hope. If they go to a genuine hypnotherapist, one who knows how to use hypnosis for curative purposes, they have a very good chance of being cured - permanently!

I also hope that some of the hypnotists who advertise treatments may read this book and realise that there is far more to hypnosis then just using it in attempts to improve symptoms and that they will be encouraged to learn true hypnotherapy. If they have a real interest in their patients they will learn to uncover and dispose of the cause of the problem thus making sure there can be no recurrence. The training courses I run in Birmingham are to the standards required by the Curative Hypnotherapy Examination Committee, the independent examining body for curative hypnotherapy.

All cases in this book are genuine, but names have, of course, been changed as have any other features of the particular case that could identify the patients involved, and extracts from letters do not refer to the cases described in that chapter.

I have only a couple
of words to say— Thank You!

(Female Age 34)

Imagination

Why does the human race have so many more problems than the rest of the animals?

Our basic anatomy and physiology are the same, our bodies work in a similar way to other mammals. Even our mental processes work along the same lines. Yet we suffer far more problems than the average animal and, while many of these problems appear to be physical, most of them have a mental cause.

Could it be that the old saying that 'genius is akin to madness' has a lot of truth in it? Could it be that as we become more and more "clever" we produce more and more problems for ourselves? Madness is imagination running riot and it is imagination above everything else that marks us out as different to all other animals. It is the power of abstract thought that has enabled us to rise above the rest of the animal kingdom: In other words, it is ideas.

When James Watt watched the lid of the kettle bouncing up and down as the water boiled he started to think, he used his imagination, he had an idea, and he developed the steam engine. He used his imagination as has every other inventor, author, composer or architect. Even people watching television are using their imagination to become involved in the programme, but each one interprets what they see in their own way. They interpret what they see in the light of their own experience, and none of them react in exactly the same way. In other words, they use their imagination. As you read the cases in this book you will realise that it is imagination that lies at the root of many problems. My patients are not reacting to WHAT happened but to their interpretation of what happened. They use their imagination on the facts and then react to the interpretation they make.

Thus, a lad of eighteen found any regular noise caused tension, dizzyness and faintness. The click of his mother's knitting needles, someone snoring, a clock ticking or a typist in a nearby office made him feel ill and he had the same problem with visual things such as disco lights, a pendulum or the flashing direction-indicators of a car.

Under hypnosis he took me back to when he was a baby in his pram in the kitchen of his parents' home. His mother was bending over him. He was getting her attention and he was happy. His mother disappeared from his view and he heard a regular noise, one he had difficulty in describing to me. This happened many times - when his mother was in view and paying him attention there was no noise, when his mother was out of sight he often heard that regular sound.

He was too young to pull himself up in the pram and look over the side thus could not see the cause of the noise. All he knew was that it symbolised that his mother's attention was not on him, and on one particular occasion when he had a slight fever and needed his mother's comfort, all he got was the noise.

He associated the noise with feeling ill and thus developed his reaction to regular sounds. The reality of the situation was that his mother (as he later found out by asking her after treatment) had taken up tapestry to keep herself occupied while she looked after him, and the sound that caused him so much distress was the sound of the needle as it went through the material she was embroidering. The fact that she had taken up this hobby to keep herself busy while keeping him company never occurred to him - his imagination told him exactly the opposite - that the noise meant she was paying him no attention, that he was abandoned when he needed her most. Then his imagination took things a stage further.

At four years old, when this reaction was embedded in his subconscious, his father brought a new clock with a glass panel in the base through which could be seen a swinging pendulum. At one end of the pendulum's stroke, as the clock ticked, the pendulum caught the light and 'flashed'. The ticking and flashing became as one and thus developed his aversion to flashing lights.

When he first came for treatment he was worried about losing his job as he had recently been moved to an office with a large ticking clock on the wall. Day after day he became ill, was unable to work more than a couple of hours and had to be sent home by mid-morning. His doctor had given him tranquilisers and a note to a psychiatrist but had also mentioned that hypnotherapy might help. After a couple of treatments the noise had become bearable although still uncomfortable. Not only was he able to work, but had given up the earphones that he used to wear at home to muffle the ticking of the clock. It took a further two sessions to find out what was causing his problem and correct his imagined interpretation of that old event. All his symptoms disappeared completely with the re-interpretation.

He had reacted in accordance with what he imagined took place not with what had really happened. Our imagination is more important, more powerful than reality which is why many patients, at the conclusion of treatment make comments like "that was crazy" or "I know it's true because I'm cured, but it's difficult to believe that something as simple as that has caused me all that trouble".

The more intelligent the person the more likely they are to develop a problem. Intelligence requires abstract thought and that needs imagination. The more highly developed the imagination, the more likely it is to go off on the wrong track. Thus with hypnotherapy we have a double difficulty: a highly developed imagination causes apprehension about the things that will be uncovered during treatment. Even people with blameless lives feel this, not realising that they have control all the time and I can only uncover what they wish and that the causes of problems are virtually always insignificant no matter how bad their symptoms. Also intelligent people are very inclined to use their intelligence during treatment which can only delay their cure. As becomes clearer in the following chapters, the problem does not lie in the intelligent part of the mind but in the part which reacts - without commonsense. The most highly intelligent will understand and leave the treatment to me without analysing themselves. Having decided that I am competent they will just relax and not interfere. But this takes real intelligence.

One highly intelligent man, a surgeon who was taking extra examinations in a specialised field, would not let me guide him even under hypnosis. He could not believe that just one incident could have caused his inability to study for his examinations as all through school and medical college he had been top of his class. I may have been a little rude to him when I told him that, if he was doing surgery on me and I kept telling him what to do, he would make a mess of the job. I told him that what he believed did not matter, he had to accept that I was the one with experience in hypnotherapy and go along with the treatment, or he was wasting my time. He had already failed this examination five times and there was only a month before he took it again so we had a time limit to work to.

His inability to concentrate went back to when he took up knitting as a child. His father thought he should be outside getting exercise and told him about a boy who had taken up knitting and concentrated so much on it that he went blind. The boy had taken little notice of the story but had filed it away in the memory of his subconscious and when he was a fully qualified surgeon, studying for this new examination, he automatically reacted even though he had completely forgotten the incident.

One of his colleagues, who knew he was always studying, put his head into the room on one occasion and said "You'll die blind". That comment - that joke - was the confirmation of the story told by his father and he then had conflict. Should he study and lose his sight or keep the ability to see by giving up concentration on his books and then failing his examination?

Quite apart from his normal desire not to become blind, surgery needs a sighted person almost more than any other occupation. So the whole purpose of his concentration became useless to him. Without conscious thought, the automatic part of his mind made him unable to concentrate in order to ward off the imagined threat to his sight. As always, imagination is more powerful than reality.

When he telephoned to say "I've passed. Thank you very much," I could not resist an "I told you so".

was very good and has brought me back my normal self.

Male Age 50

Saving Dad's Life

"What do you mean, get at the cause?" asked Susan. "I know the cause of being overweight - I eat too much".

"Why?" I queried.

"Because I feel like eating all the time."

"Why?"

"I don't know".

"Is it a compulsion?" I asked. She agreed it was. "Something compels you to overeat, so when you stop and think about it there must be a reason, a cause. Isn't that so? You don't feel compelled to do things without any reason."

"OK David, I'll go along with that, but what sort of cause could there be and if there is one how do you find out what it is?"

"I'm going to ignore the second part of your question," I told her. "It takes too long to explain and it's much quicker to demonstrate. I'll try to answer the first part of the question briefly. First of all, we know that this excessive amount of food is not a physical necessity. If it was, you would not be storing all that excess fat, you'd be burning it up".

"I'm with you so far", said Susan.

"If it's not a physical need", I continued, "then it must be mental, it is in your mind. Yet your conscious mind tells you that you don't want to eat this much, you don't want to be fat. You have even told me that you sometimes get a snack ready then tell yourself you don't need it, put it away, and only minutes later feel compelled to get it out again and eat it. Your conscious mind is in conflict with this compulsion. Your conscious mind certainly wants to get rid of it otherwise you wouldn't be sitting here, paying me good money to help you lose weight. So although the compulsion is mental, it isn't in your conscious mind. Your conscious mind is trying to stop you overeating, therefore it has to be in another part of your mind, your subconsious, your computer".

"Are you telling me I'm a robot - computer-controlled?" Susan was quite indignant at the thought. "I'm not a machine, I have free will, I can make my own decisions".

"Agreed", I said, "but you go against your own decisions about eating. Tell me, can you control your body sweating when you get too hot? That is an automatic reaction caused by your computer to help cool your body. Can you control your shivering when you get too cold? That helps to warm your body. Can you control your feelings of anger...?" Susan jumped in there.

"Yes. I never give in to anger, I always control it."

"Wait a minute Susan", I told her. "You can control what you do about that feeling of anger, but you can't control the feeling itself. You can make a conscious decision not to curse or swear or hit out, but you can't use your conscious mind to get rid of that feeling of anger. That you have no control over, yet it IS mental. It is obviously not in your conscious mind, neither is the feeling of sadness, or jealousy, or love, or despair, or any of your other emotions. They are all in your computer and cause certain uncontrollable reactions. Such as sadness making tears come to your eyes even if you don't want to cry in front of someone else, embarrassment making you blush, even though you don't want to get red in the face. You can't use your conscious mind to tell those reactions to go away and expect them to disappear. There are certain physical reactions that you cannot control, like blushing".

"This is fascinating, David, but what could cause the physical reaction of needing to eat?"

"There are hundreds of reasons but I don't want to put ideas into your head at this stage. Under hypnosis you are going to tell me the reason. Although it isn't in your conscious mind, under hypnosis, your subconscious will let me know".

"How will I tell you if I don't even know that there is a cause?"

"Under hypnosis", I replied, "we shall relax your conscious mind which normally filters and interprets all information before it gets to your computer. When that's relaxed I can talk to your computer directly. Just like any computer we can put it on a particular programme, in your case the programme which compels you to overeat, and instruct it to take us back to the first piece of information that started the programme. I know that you don't consciously know the reason but it is there in your computer and can be uncovered".

"But what good will uncovering the reason do? Will that stop me overeating?"

"Not just uncovering it, no, but remember we are dealing with a computer which is giving an incorrect reaction, and the only way that you can get a wrong answer from a computer is if it has been given incorrect data. Whatever the incident was that started this programme, it must be some wrong information, probably a misinterpretation of an event that has happened before you started to become overweight. When we find out what this misinformation is, we can correct it - because it is misinformation we can correct it - so that your computer can react as it should from there on".

Susan looked disbelieving but I told her there would not be time for treatment unless we started.

When she had first entered my consulting room she had told me that she had a very attractive figure until just after she had a baby. Shortly after that her weight had shot up from 8.5 stone (119 lbs) before pregnancy to 19 stone (276 lbs) which is what it was that day. She blamed this on a hormone imbalance and from this I assumed that she had been having medical treatment. Susan confirmed that a doctor had discovered a hormone imbalance and had been giving her treatment to correct it but without success and I pointed out to her that she must therefore have been counteracting what the doctor was giving her - she was reacting by making the imbalance worse so that the doctor's medication was ineffective because her subconscious wanted her to be overweight and did not want the imbalance corrected. This was where our discussion had started.

On this occasion I took Susan into that very beautiful state of relaxation that we call hypnosis so that she would realise that it was only relaxation and would be aware of everything that went on so there would be no worries or apprehension when coming for future treatments. I ended this first session by giving her some direct suggestions about wanting to eat less, needing to eat less and before she left she asked whether I could not just treat her with direct instructions in this way. I explained that it may be possible but, if initially effective, was unlikely to have a long lasting result. While it may reduce her weight a little it was highly unlikely to achieve the large weight loss she wanted as the stronger my instructions became the more resistance her subconscious would put up. For some reason it *needed* to keep her fat.

I also pointed out that even if my direct instructions were effective in making her lose some of her excess weight, the cause of her problems would still be there and would gradually erode my instructions. Her need to be fat was stronger than an outsider's suggestions to reduce her appetite. The only way to cure her was to find out why her subconscious compelled her to overeat and, having put that right, she should never become overweight again.

As normal, on the second occasion that people come for treatment, I start to find out the reason why they have their particular problem. Having once again relaxed Susan into hypnosis, I started to question her and found out that the cause of her overeating was something to do with having her baby. It also had something to do with her mother. The desire to overeat had not started when she had the baby but it had started only a couple of days afterwards which was when her mother died. Over the next three or four treatments the whole story gradually came out from Susan's subconscious mind.

"Was there a connection between having the baby, your mother dying and the overeating compulsion?" I asked her.

"Yes".

"Did you overeat because your mother didn't want you to have the baby?" --- "No".

"Did your mother give that baby a lot of attention?" --- "Yes".

"Were you jealous of the attention it got?" --- "No".

"If you hadn't had the baby would you be overeating now?" --- "No".

"If your mother hadn't died would you be overeating now?" --- "No".

"If your mother died before you had the baby would you be overeating now?" --- "No".

If your mother had died a year after you had the baby would you be overeating now?" --- "No?".

"Is your overeating due to the fact that your mother died so soon after you had the baby?" --- "Yes".

This particular technique of questioning which can only give 'yes' or 'no' answers is rather slow but can be very accurate.

"So you put on weight because your mother died so soon after you had the baby?" --- "Yes".

"Do you feel responsible for your mother's death?" There was a hesitation here, then the answer ---"Yes".

"Do you believe that having the baby was the cause of your mother's death?" --- "Yes".

"Now, Susan," I said, "I must find out exactly why you have that idea, where that idea came from, what caused it. Was it some words that someone said to you?" --- "Yes".

I had in my mind the 'old wives tale' about 'one coming into the world and one going out', but I could not let my own ideas or feelings intrude on the treatment.

"Was this thing said to you by someone in your family?" --- "Yes".

"Was it said to you by your mother?" --- "Yes".

"I need to know the exact words, Susan, I need to know the precise words. You must go back to the very instant that these words were used that have caused you to overeat. I want to know the exact words. So go back to that very instant that these words were said and hear them again clearly and exactly and then tell me precisely what those words were."

Susan lay back in her chair looking very relaxed indeed, without any movement at all. Then she said "Mum, I'm pregnant". .... "Oh Sue! You'll be the death of me".

"Was it those words which you have just uttered that have caused the problem?" --- "Yes".

"When you told your mother that you were pregnant, did she use those exact words? And is that why, when your mother died almost immediately after you had your baby, you felt responsible for her death?"

"Yes".

"Is guilt the emotion that lies at the root of your problem?" -- "No".

And so we went on, gradually sifting, gradually eliminating, gradually finding out more and more of the reason that lay at the root of her problem, until it emerged that the subconscious part of her mind - that computer, that logical part of her mind which has no commonsense - had connected the words "You'll be the death of me", uttered by her mother with the fact that her mother did die almost immediately after she had had the baby. Being logical it took the next step from there - that if one baby kills one of her parents, then another baby will kill her other parent!

Her subconscious did not want her to be responsible for the death of her father and went into logical action to prevent her becoming pregnant. It knew that contraception was not 100% effective, certainly not effective enough to rely on when her father's life was at stake. Liking sex as much as she did, it knew she would not be able to continually refuse her husband, that she would eventually weaken and have intercourse with him. But it also knew that her husband did not like fat women and she was certain in her subconscious that if she put on a lot of weight he would not want to have sex with her.

Once Susan's subconscious had worked out that the logical steps it had taken were based on an original bit of mis-information (that having the baby killed her mother) it was a simple matter to get her subconscious to alter that automatic reaction and for the last couple of sessions Susan readily accepted the suggestions that she would become full on a small amount of food. By the end of six treatments she had lost 25 lbs and in the 14 months since then we have weighed her each time she comes up to our allied clinic for Body Massage. She has been steadily losing weight without further treatment, without dieting, without denying herself anything that she wanted to eat, and she now weighs only 127 lbs having lost a total of 149 lbs without any effort on her part at all.

Near the end of the treatments, when Susan realised just how easy it was to lose weight and understood why she had become fat in the first place, her words were, "How can anyone be that crazy and still be sane?" But, insanity or craziness does not come into it. It was purely the automatic part of her mind, that computer using its logic

Dear David,

I have just completed your six week course for weight reduction, during which time I have attained a weight loss of 1 stone 4 lbs. Not only am I thrilled at the weight loss but I am "over the moon" with the really healthy, lively feeling I have. I never feel tired or lethargic and I find I have more patience with other people, more self confidence and on the whole am a

Female Age 30

all for the success you have achieved so far in my quest for a weight reduction. From 12st 6lbs to 9st 11lb in 7months can't be bad, I am now lighter by 7lb than I have been for 25 years. The

Female Age 44

My weight is still coming off slow but sure, but nevertheless as I mentioned to you during the sessions I feel much happier about my attitude towards food, and it no longer takes priority in my life. This is a great weight off my mind as well as my body.

Female Age 22

brought down to 7st. 13lb.

Female Age 27

Just a quick note to say a big thank you for solving my weight problem. I have already lost 7lb and I am certain that the rest of my excess weight will soon follow.

My eating habits have changed for the better and I feel much more confident now, not only about my weight but about other things too.

Once again thanks for everything

Female Age 21

Dear Mr Lesser

Thankyou very much for all the help you gave me over the past month or so with my weight problem

Female Age 41

The Onion Picker

"I told you there was no magical cure, only a logical one." I told Mr Hunt. "It is no good expecting a tremendous change just having been relaxed once, we haven't even begun to find out the cause of your problem yet. You've had your lack of confidence for over 40 years and it has been getting steadily worse. The fact that after only one week it appears a fraction better is a tremendous step forward. Many people feel little benefit until after two or three treatments and, of course, a great number of them feel no benefit at all until we have found out and corrected the cause, as the cause is too strong for them to react to direct suggestions that I give to them."

"But, I thought hypnosis......."
I interrupted him, "If you think that a couple of sessions will cause a miracle then your knowledge of hypnosis has been given to you by people who have never experienced it and are ignorant of it's effects".

"Look," I went on, "If you broke your leg and went to hospital, the first thing they would do is paper work - name, address, age, religion and so on. Does that help your leg to heal? Or ease the pain?"

"Of course not, but I suppose that they need those details."

"Next they will take you to the X-ray department, does that picture help your leg?"

"No, but it helps them know what they are dealing with so that they can deal with the broken leg more efficiently."

"In other words, it is a necessary preparation for a proper job to be done on you?" I asked him.

"Yes."

"When the experts tell you that preparation is necessary you accept it because it IS necessary, even if it doesn't help your leg directly. Why can't you accept that after the hundreds of people that I have treated successfully, I too have some knowledge of what I am doing and that I also need to find out the best method of treating you? I am not dealing with a broken leg, I am dealing with something that is unique - your mind - and not a single person in the world has the same experiences or the identical problem to you, unlike a broken leg which is a standard injury with standard treatment."

"I told you that it will take around half-a-dozen treatments to cure your problem, and that includes the preparation time. If after forty years with the problem getting worse and worse, you can't be sufficiently patient to go through only a total of four hours treatment, if after all this time of steadily diminishing confidence, you are not prepared to wait just a couple of months to have it cured permanently, then you are wasting my time and your money. You must allow me to proceed in the way that I have proved time after time. You told me when you came that your knowledge of hypnosis and hypnotherapy was almost nil, so leave it to somebody who does know. We have to work methodically, so can we start work now, instead of wasting further treatment time which is only delaying your cure and costing you more?"

I had deliberately been tough with Mr Hunt because his lack of confidence was so great that he did not even have sufficient confidence in himself to believe that a cure was possible. This, of course, is one of the biggest problems with people who suffer a lack of confidence and even more so with people in depression. The symptom of depression tells people that they cannot be helped, because if they knew that they were getting help they would automatically feel less depressed. But the depression overrides any feeling of help that they may be getting. Although Mr Hunt was not in depression he was suffering very badly from a lack of confidence, almost verging on depression, and many forms of depression are nothing more nor less than an absolute lack of confidence.

Actually, Mr Hunt was an easy case. After I had shown him my impatience in this way he was prepared to accept and, this being his second treatment, I started the process of uncovering the cause of his problem. He went straight back to the age of four, in the back garden of his house, helping his parents to pull up the weeds. On this occasion, because of the time we had wasted at the beginning of the session, I was able to find out little more than the fact that he was happy while he was helping his parents weed the garden and apparently nothing unusual happened.

At the following session we made more progress, in fact we virtually finished his treatment. Apparently his parents had given up weeding to go into the house and have a cup of tea but he had stayed in the garden happily pulling up the unwanted growth. Being only a four year old, after being on his own for a while he got a little bit fed up and decided that, because his neighbours were nice people, he would do them a favour. So he went next door into their garden to help them by doing some weeding and he pulled up all his neighbours onions!

When his parents returned to the garden and found out what he had done, he was punished. Whether or not he was punished by words or by being slapped, I never bothered to find out - the punishment itself was enough. Whatever sort it was, that punishment lay at the root of his problem.

Mr Hunt had been doing something that was not only NOT wrong, but it was definitely right. It was actually helpful to other people. He did something that was right and proper and was punished for it. Ever since then, when he was carrying on his normal life, doing things that he knew were right, he has had a feeling of anticipation - was he going to be punished again? Was he really doing right? He questioned his ability, his every move; was it really right? How could it go wrong? Would there be some form of punishment coming? He eventually became unable to make decisions and completely lost all confidence in himself. Now, however, he was able to look back at that whole incident with the eyes of an adult of forty eight years old and able to correct the reactions that it had caused. He was able to use his commonsense to correct his computers logic.

This is exactly the kind of incident that lies at the root of very many problems of self-confidence. Sometime, somewhere in the past people have done something that they did not realise was wrong. It is more than likely that, basically, it was not wrong, but their parents, or the customs of the civilization in which they live, force them into believing that it is wrong when their instincts tell them it is right.

A good example of such an incident is that of a girl in her twenties, a very retiring girl with a tremendous lack of confidence in herself. This incident also happened at the age of four when she was at the house of an aunt. She was talking to her cousin, Phillip, in the bathroom. The talk was innocent enough and we followed her through the whole of that day without anything coming to the surface because she had omitted to tell me the embarrassing part of that story, purely and simply because the subconscious did not want her to see it. The following week she took me back once again to the same day and the same time in the bathroom. Once again we ran through the conversation between her and Phillip. Then she let the suppressed memory come to the fore. Phillip wanted to go to the toilet and, being as innocent as she was at the age of four, he just went over to the toilet , undid his trousers and started to urinate. She had never seen anybody doing it standing up before, so she walked to the side of him to see how he was doing it. For the first time ever she saw a penis. It fascinated her, so she put out her hand and touched it. He had no objection, and they started to talk about it and for the first time he realized that she did not have one. She therefore took her pants down to demonstrate to him and he touched her. This completely natural exploration of each other went on for a few minutes and then it went out of both their heads. But on a future occasion when she was visiting her aunt's house again, the two of them were in the garden and this time she wanted to relieve herself. She went behind a bush which screened her from the house and he stood and watched her. As so often happens when one sees running water, one wants to pass water themselves. Once again he undid his trousers and both of them were behind the bush, watching each other relieving themselves, when the two older sisters of my patient found them and threatened to tell the girl's mother. From the age of four up until her mid-twenties the threat was still hanging over her as it had never actually been carried out. She still has the fear that when she does something that she considers natural, there is going to be punishment, and what she and her cousin did *was* completely natural. We encourage our children to be curious, to ask questions, to find out what and why and how things work, except in one sphere, that of the difference in sexes. Why is this so? Why is this treated so secretly?

As a child's curiosity is whetted by the explanations given to it; it is only natural that it should try and find out, having been given a verbal explanation. If it has not had a verbal explanation and finds out something peculiar for itself, as in this case, then what is more natural for a human being, with human curiosity, to investigate and find out? Unfortunately, investigation of sexual matters by a child runs straight against the present-day customs of this country - hence this girl's problem, a problem of confidence and, as she said in the initial consultation, she felt ill-at-ease in the company of men, certainly if she was alone with them. She had never had more than one date with anyone because men were the cause of the threat which was still hanging over her and also, they had an anatomical difference which she must not see, which she must not touch, she must not, in fact, even find out about in case something awful would happen to her.

I am happy to say I have
80% confidence now thanks
for every thing

Male Age 49

Dear David,
Thanks for your help in gaining
my confidence. I feel like a new person
has emerged from your treatments.
My other problems have also been
resolved. Blushing, sexual, etc.
Thank You

Female Age 23

I thank you for what
you have done for me, I am very
grateful, & I know it has worked
& I feel very confident now.

Male Age 9

Creating Reality

Hypnotherapy is searching the memory to uncover misinterpretations in order to correct them, and to find out where imagination has caused someone to create their own personal reality. The child learning to ride a bicycle feels secure because his parent has a hand underneath the saddle steadying the machine. He believes that he is secure, and he can steadily turn the pedals and steer without wobbling because of this security. When the parent sees that the child is managing to cycle steadily he lets go of the saddle, but the child still believes that there is someone there to support him and cycles on confidently. It is only the child's imagination which tells him he is safe. He believes he is still supported, but that belief becomes his reality and he cycles without any tendency to fall off.

After a few seconds the child realises it cannot hear its parents footsteps and that no-one is supporting him. His imagination tells him that without that support he will fall; his confidence disappears because he 'knows' he will fall without support; he imagines he will fall. His imagination creates the reality, and he falls.

From the moment his parent let go of the saddle until he fell off the bike, the true reality did not change. The only thing which changed was the child's belief. He believed that he was supported and thus cycled confidently, then realised that he was not supported and fell off. To start with he imagined he could cycle, and he cycled; then he imagined he would fall and nothing could keep him on that bike. We create reality out of our imagination every day of our lives. When meeting someone for the first time you may have an intuitive feeling that she dislikes you. There are no hard facts to go on, just the feelings you have. If you feel they dislike you, then your reaction is to develop a dislike for them. As soon as they sense the dislike in you, they will react, quite naturally, by not liking you. Their dislike is now genuine, even though it started in your unfounded imagination in the first place. It was your misinterpretation of something about that person - their appearance, their mannerisms, whatever it may have been - which caused them to have a genuine dislike for you.

Virtually every case in this book is based on a similar misinterpretation. One girl became overweight due to an incident when she was eight years old and her younger sister knocked her dinner off the table. None of the family realised that it was as a result of a fit; nobody had any idea that she had a brain tumor and that within a year she would be dead! The sequence of events in my patient's mind was that her sister pushed her food onto the floor and became ill and died. She interpreted the illness and the death as a punishment for her sister's action. She did not want that sort of punishment, and so she ate everything that was available to her. She had a compulsion to eat to save herself from similar fate, and she became very considerably overweight.

Had she known the true sequence of events: that the illness was already there, that the illness had caused a fit and that pushing the food off the table was an involuntary action, her reactions would have been different. It was only her wrong interpretation of events which caused her to become fat.

A person who suffers a lack of confidence enters a situation knowing that they can not succeed and because of this 'knowledge' they will, naturally, not give that situation full effort. Without full effort they will not fully succeed, and the failure, or partial failure increases their lack of confidence. It reinforces their belief that they can not succeed so that the next situation that they have to face, they face with even less confidence than the one before. This will lead to a greater failure and an even greater lack of confidence for the next situation. They continually reinforce their original belief, and because they can not achieve they can develop tension or anxiety, lack of interest in their job or sexual problems. There are many ways in which a lack of confidence can affect someone and it is useless to tell somebody who is suffering from a lack of confidence, whether under hypnosis or not, that they are going to be more confident. Take the case of the Onion Picker, earlier on in this book who, while doing something helpful and right, was then punished for that action. To tell that man that he is going to be more confident, without any attempt to find out the reason for his lack of confidence, will only bring about the automatic reaction of the sub-conscious, "No, I am not going to be confident, because when I am confident, I am punished."

The woman who came for weight loss, went back under hypnosis, first of all, to the age of twelve and told me that she experienced embarrassment and anger against herself at the time that the incident took place:

"Why are you angry?"

"My period started, I don't want it."

"Why don't you want it?"

"I don't want to become an adult".

"Why don't you want to become an adult?"

"Because I can't go swimming then."

"You mean you can't go swimming when you have your periods?"

"Yes. If I put on weight, my periods will stop, and then I could swim. I'm a good swimmer. I want to be a champion".

"I want to know," I told her, "exactly how you got the idea that putting on weight can stop your periods".

"Mary told me. She's in my class."

"What was it that Mary told you? I want the exact words that made you believe that putting on weight would stop your periods."

"Mrs Shepherd's having a baby. She's very fat. Mary told me that Mrs Shepherd's periods had stopped."

Naturally, it was true that if the teacher was pregnant, then her periods would have stopped. But my patient used her own interpretation because of her lack of knowledge about pregnancy. Her interpretation was that putting on weight had caused her teacher's periods to cease therefore, if she became overweight her periods would stop and she could become a champion swimmer. Because of her dislike of periods, because of how they were stopping her from becoming a swimming champion, she developed a dread of her periods. She created pre-menstrual tension and period pains, all of which, together with her excess weight, have disappeared after treatment.

Many times I am asked what sort of things can be cured by hypnotherapy. One can give a list as long as this whole book, but there is also a short answer: Anyone with an incorrect reaction of any sort at all, can be helped by hypnotherapy and not only helped, but completely and permanently *cured*. An incorrect reaction, whether it is a mental reaction, as we call it, or what appears to be a purely physical one, has to be the result of incorrect information in the person's computer. People believe that things like asthma are purely physical, yet they always have a mental cause, that an allergy to certain foods can also be classed as a physical problem, yet, again it always has a mental cause. The secret of hypnotherapy is to remember that everything in the body is controlled by the mind. Everything in the body will function normally assuming that there is no physical damage, unless the controlling computer has been misprogrammed and this can cause anything from arthritis to infertility from depression to obesity and from alcoholism to tinnitus. The imagination misinterprets something, it creates its own reality and then it reacts in accordance with that reality.

The girl who could spend no more than a few minutes in the sun without developing an uncomfortable rash and desperately wanted to get a sun-tan, was reacting to an incident which took place when she was three years old, on a beach. She wandered away from her parents and got lost. Not only was she frightened, but she was so frightened that she ended up by wetting herself.

Although she was now in her late twenties and had no trouble in controlling her bladder, the sunshine was making her develop the rash so that she would not go out and enjoy herself in case she became lost or wet herself again. The true reality was that she was a sensible normal adult, unlikely to get lost on a beach and highly unlikely ever to have a similar 'accident' in her life, but she was reacting as she would have done if she was still three years old. Her reality was that sunshine meant enjoyment, enjoyment meant getting lost, getting lost meant embarrassing herself by losing control of her bladder. She reacted to that reality by preventing herself going out in the sun and developed a rash to achieve this end.

is my arthritis. You told me it might take some time before there would be any improvement. Well you will be pleased to hear that one of my joints is much better and I know it's due to your help.

So once again I'll say thank you so very much I'm very grateful to you for helping me.

Female Age 47

I came to you suffering from Arthritis, Nervous Tension and having difficulty sleeping, at the same taking various tablets to relieve pain and assist in my sleeping.

Its gives me great satisfaction to inform you that after 20 years of Nervous Tension 5 years Arthritis your course of Therapy at your Centre removed the ailments you treated me for — HENCE NO MORE TABLETS.

I am confident, definite in my approach to every day tasks, relaxed at all times and I also enjoy a very relaxed sleep.

Male Age 63

Its you know, for years I have suffered from a very painful rash whenever I sat out in the sun and consequently have remained snow white instead of having a nice tan.

I have now turned a lovely golden bronze after holidaying in Cyprus back in March and I've still got the colour! It seems so

Silly that an incident that happened so many years ago & could have been responsible for the physical effect it has had on me. All I can say is thanks & roll on next Summer!!

Female Age 28

Hypnosis, Hypnotherapy or Curative Hypnotherapy?

What is hypnotherapy? The answer to this is a very short one or a very long one. The short answer is that hypnotherapy is the use of hypnosis for therapeutic purposes - i.e. to relieve people of symptoms so far as is possible.

The long answer requires an explanation starting with hypnosis itself.

Like electricity, no-one is completely sure exactly what hypnosis is. However, like electricity, we can put it to very good use. Previously, I have tried to demonstrate the difference between the conscious and the sub-conscious parts of the mind. The conscious part of the mind is that part which analyses and makes decisions, whereas the subconscious holds all the memories and all the reactions, and is mainly there to keep a person healthy, happy and protected. It is the subconscious which decides when gastric juices will be released into the stomach to digest the food, it is the part which decides how fast your heart should beat according to the energy being burned up or the tension being experienced. It is the part which causes hair to grow on your head and nails on your toes, and is responsible for the regeneration of cells in your body. It thus lies at the root of all sorts of problems and illness, even such things as cancer, which is gradually being recognised as having 'stress' as a cause.

The subconscious is like a computer - it reacts. It does not think, it leaves that to the conscious mind. It reacts in accordance with its programming, relating all incidents to the best way of keeping you healthy, of keeping you happy and keeping you protected from danger. The conscious mind is rather like a computer operator, taking incoming information, putting it into the computer, and then carrying out the actions that the computer thinks is best in those circumstances. Where those actions are not under conscious control, but under the direct control of the subconscious, then that part of the mind will carry those actions out automatically. We call these automatic reactions whether they be panic, tension, depression, fear of thunder or aches and pains which apparently have no physical cause.

As these reactions are in our computer we need, during treatment, to be able to contact our computer without having our words reinterpreted by the computer operator. If someone has wrong information in their computer, the memory banks will feed this misinformation to the computer operator (i.e. the patient himself). The computer operator will measure the therapist's words against the information being fed to it from the computer's memory banks and will analyse, will reinterpret and reject much of what the therapist says. This is where the use of hypnosis cuts down the treatment time to a fraction of that necessary for other methods as hypnosis is essentially relaxation of the conscious mind, that is to say, relaxation of the critical and decision-making part of the mind. The patient is aware of what is said, of everything that is going on and has the ability to involve the conscious mind and to analyse and criticise, but a cooperative patient will not do so unless, of course, something is said that is in direct conflict with what they believe or feel.

Thus, hypnosis is persuading the conscious mind to take a rest, to watch what is going on, to hear but not to interfere. In other words, the secret of hypnosis is acceptance by the patient of the meaning of the words used by the therapist.

Once the conscious mind is relaxed, the therapist can talk directly to the computer without the computer operator altering any of the words. Our words can go directly into the subconscious, and the subconscious can respond directly to the therapist. Hypnosis is purely this state of relaxation of the critical and analytical faculties. It is a state in which one is fully conscious and fully aware, but so relaxed that one cannot be bothered to analyse or criticise, except if a real need arises.

Hypnotherapy is using this beautiful state to help alleviate the person's problems. There are many people who have set up in practice as hypnotherapists with the ability to use words to relax people and treat their symptoms, but one must be careful of the results to be expected from this sort of treatment. Remember - we are dealing with a computer and a computer that has already been programmed - a computer that already has an answer in it. No computer can produce a different answer to the one with which it has already been programmed. Although direct suggestion may work to alleviate problems to some extent, while the reason for the problems is still there in the patient's mind, that reason will gradually erode away the direct suggestions, or alternatively, a patient's computer will seek another set of symptoms because it has a need to feel guilty, a need to feel tense, a need to suffer headaches, a need for punishment, a need to be overweight or to suffer from a lack of confidence.

The hypnotherapist who confines himself or herself to removing symptoms can, in many cases, cause greater problems for that patient by making them develop a worse set of symptoms to replace the ones treated in the first place.

Curative hypnotherapy is, as its name implies, *curing* the problem. Going back to find out the *cause* of the problem, finding out where the misinformation, or the misinterpretation, has gone into the computer, then reinterpreting and altering the original programme in a logical way that is acceptable to the logic of the computer. Once the *cause* has been dealt with in this way, there is no need to treat the symptoms at all. The subconscious is there to protect, to keep you happy and healthy, and once the cause has been corrected, the subconscious will automatically correct the reactions.

Go back to the chapter on the Onion Picker. Remember how this man had done something as a child that he thought was good and helpful and had been punished. He had been questioning his actions from there on. When he was doing things that were good he was wondering where the punishment was going to come from until he was unable to make a decision as to whether his actions were right or wrong and a complete lack of confidence ensued. To take a man like that and to treat him with direct suggestion (in other words, telling him that he was going to be confident) would be a waste of time in the long run because the automatic reaction of his computer is, "No. I am not going to be confident because when I was confident, I was punished. Being without confidence has saved me from punishments - I will not be confident."

Where hypnotherapy is used for simple symptom removal many people experience replacement symptoms. Unfortunately the process may take several months and therefore many people do not associate the original problem with the one that they develop later. The nail biter who, months after stopping nail biting, with the help of hypnosis, developed a facial tic, had no idea that the two problems were connected. The person who was treated for blushing did not connect the eczema that he developed on the back of his hands with his original problem because approximately one year had gone by, but he still had a need to show the world that he was guilty. If he could not show it in his face by blushing, he showed it on the back of his hands, which is the only other part of the body that is always exposed to public gaze. The lady who lost the worst of her tension after treatment but became grossly obese was able to date her ravenous appetite to about the time she had hypnosis for her tension without making any connection between the two events, yet her obesity was causing her great distress and this distress created tension every bit as bad as the original tension for which she had treatment.

It is unfortunate that most hypnotists using this state of relaxation for symptom removal are never aware of their failures or the alternative symptoms they are creating. If a person rejects the direct suggestions because the computer cannot accept two answers to any single problem, they just stop going for treatment, and, in many cases, the 'therapists' believe they have stopped because of successful treatment.

The patients who develop alternative symptoms start right back at the beginning again with a round of doctors, pills and so on before they ever consider going back to a hypnotherapist. If they should go back to the same hypnotherapist, he will never find out the cause of the problem, will never realize that it was he who actually caused this secondary problem. He will give just straight forward symptom treatment once again, creating possible further problems in the future.

When I consider the simplicity of curative hypnotherapy, I feel a disgust for these people who will take money for such so-called treatments without any care for the problems they may cause in the future.

My advice to potential patients is to ask questions. Will your therapist find out the cause of your problems and correct it? Does he have that ability? If you get an answer that satisfies you, then make sure that no later than your second visit, the process of going back and finding out the cause is started. Do not expect this to be done in a single session, but, if your therapist has the ability, it will show by the second session. If, on that visit, there is no sign of the therapist knowing how to tackle the problem correctly, then find yourself a genuine curative hypnotherapist.

It is possible with direct suggestion to partially alleviate symptoms, but usually only on a temporary basis. Six months ago, a girl with depression was brought to me by her mother. Her mother told me that a year previously she had been to a doctor who had cured her depression then.

I asked her mother - "If this doctor cured her, why is she here for treatment today?" Obviously, the doctor only helped her symptoms temporarily and gradually the need for her depression, because this was the basic programming, overrode the direct suggestion that the doctor had given her under hypnosis. The doctor may have called it a 'cure', her mother also used the word, but the patient knew better!

Having made the above comments, we are still entitled to call use of direct suggestion in this way hypnotherapy, because it does have a therapeutic use, but genuine curative hypnotherapy means relaxing the conscious mind so that we can talk to the computer, and then getting it to go back along the programme which is causing the symptoms until it uncovers what first started that programme. Because an incorrect reaction has to be caused by incorrect information, we can then correct it and having then corrected it, the symptoms will disappear without having any direct suggestion to help them on their way.

Curative hypnotherapy means exactly what the words imply, that you will be cured, that never again can the same misinformation cause similar problems.

There is, of course, another aspect to people who treat symptoms only. One lady who came to me for treatment was a compulsive hair puller. She was steadily pulling hairs out of her head. When I went back to find out the cause of her problem I found out that originally she had been a nail biter and she had gone to a local hypnotist who had cured her of biting her nails, but she had a reason for the tension that was causing her nail biting and more than that, she had a reason to have the physical sign to the outside world that she was suffering from this tension. Her nail biting had been a visible sign and when the hypnotist stopped her biting her nails she took up something which was a lot worse and developed the habit of pulling her hair out so that she had bald patches all over her head. Had this hypnotist understood what he was doing he would have gone back, he would have found out the reason for her tension and corrected that instead of giving her worse symptoms than she had in the beginning.

There is no doubt that curative hypnotherapy can cure many

mental and physical problems. It is not the answer to every single problem and even with people who have problems that are curable one cannot always guarantee success. The success rate is extremely high but because the people do not feel a benefit from the first treatment, quite a percentage never follow through to the end of the treatment. There are also people who do not wish to be cured. Because their problem may be getting special attention from members of their family - maybe they are being treated like an invalid and enjoying being pampered in this way. They will balance their problem against the benefits that their problem is bringing and in some cases will not be cured because their loss will be bigger that their gain.

Those who can find a therapist who is acceptable to them (and no-one will accept hypnosis from someone they strongly dislike or distrust) have a very high chance of being cured of their problem. But to ensure a genuine cure, to ensure that the symptoms will not come back or that the patient will not develop alternative, sometimes more distressing, symptoms it is necessary that they find a genuine curative hypnotherapist. At the back of the book I have listed the address of the examination committee which has been set up to weed out the hypnotists from the curative hypnotherapists.

I have previously tried to demonstrate that similar symptoms between patients do not necessarily mean similar incidents lying at the root of the problem and that similar causes can create completely different symptoms.

A couple of cases of bed-wetters may demonstrate the point:

The man who developed the problem of keeping his erection and the lady who developed tension both had bed-wetting at the root of the problem, although it was not bed-wetting itself that had caused the problem, it was their mothers' words.

The man was aged twenty seven when he came for treatment and had been told by his mother that he would never grow into a 'big boy' if he kept wetting the bed. Naturally enough, in accepting his mothers' words he developed a problem with his erection which was easily cured.

The lady, on the other hand, was told by her mother that she was a dirty girl and that 'no-one loves dirty little girls'. She developed tension which was greatest when she was with her friends. After all, no-one can love you if they are not a friend. It was also this feeling that had led to her divorce and to her living for a time with a man who was a drunkard because although she 'knew' that he could not love her at least it was someone who needed her.

This lady gave me temporary disappointment after we found out her problem and corrected it. She was feeling less tense and steadily improving. She had made an appointment for her final treatment and came in a few days early to tell me that she was not going to keep that appointment because, since her last treatment with me, she had been to her doctor to tell him that she no longer needed tranquilizers. The doctor has persuaded her to go to a psychiatric clinic. He admitted that she was obviously better than she had been but still had tension. I pointed out to her that she had suffered tension for well over thirty years and she could not expect to get rid of all of her habit within about four weeks. She had already told me that she had decided that she would get a job to enlarge her circle of friends and I pointed out to her that the main symptoms had been disposed of. She had told me at the consultation that her tension was worse when she was with friends, so there was no way that she was going to deliberately set out to make new friends if that was going to create additional tension in her. She understood what I was saying but the status of her doctor was too strong. She was indeed still suffering from tension, although this was tremendously reduced and I could see that it was on its way to leaving her entirely. Without any suggestion from me, she had decided to get a job as she wanted to make new friends. She knew she did not need her tablets, again without any suggestion from me. What better signs could there be of change in her? Yet she felt she had to go along with her doctor's recommendation.

Three months later, she rang to make another appointment with me. She told me that she had attended the psychiatric unit only twice, realised that they were not helping her and, feeling more confident and less tense within herself, had stopped going. She had felt the improvement in herself since the last time she had come for treatment and she wanted the final session to finish her treatment. So we took her into hypnosis again and we checked that she had lost all the detrimental effects of her mother's words and that there was no other cause for the tension from which she had been suffering.

Since that day, I have had no direct communication with that lady but I know she must be better because three people with varying problems have come for treatment on her recommendation.

Bed-wetting itself is very often the means of a child obtaining the attention it feels it is not getting from its parents, but sometimes bed-wetting can restart in adult life. Like the lady of thirty-seven who came with this problem which had started two years previously. After the usual consultation and explanations we started to find out the cause of her problem and we went back to a visit to a hypnotist to whom she had gone in the hope that her snoring could be cured.

Although this practitioner was able to take my patient into a state of relaxation, he had no idea of how to use that state advantageously. He had enabled her to stop snoring by direct suggestion, but her snoring had been a need and she had, therefore, developed alternative symptoms of bed-wetting which were far worse than the original problem. So we had to go back to find out the reason for her snoring in the first place. We went back to the age of twenty-five. Her firm had sent her on a special course and arranged accommodation for her at a small country inn. She did not like the owner of the establishment and that night she went to bed and found that there was no lock on the door. She had a feeling that he might come in and attempt to have sex with her. Her snoring was a defence. She believed that no man would like to sleep with a woman who snored. This lady's job was travelling up and down the country training members of her company's staff, always sleeping in different places and, once established, snoring became a habit although she only became aware of it when somebody in one hotel made a comment about the noise coming from the adjoining room the night before. It was then that she visited the hypnotist and her snoring was relieved. She then had no defence against somebody who might want to come to her bed so her subconscious looked for alternative means to keep people out of her bed and a wet bed was obviously a very good defence indeed, although it caused her a lot of anguish because of continually sleeping in hotels where others had to make her bed.

It appeared to me that there was a reason why she had this fear of the man at the first inn coming into her bedroom, why she had this unnatural expectation. At the inn where her snoring first developed the same man had been in charge for many years. The company that my patient worked for only employed females in her job and had regularly used the same hostelry for accommodation of their staff without any unusual occurrences. It seemed to me that she had an unnatural fear about sex so I decided that I should bring her into full alertness at this stage, explain what I felt and ask whether she wanted this unnatural fear treated, because that was what lay at the root of her problem. She told me that she did not feel frightened about having sex, but she had never had any inclination for any sort of sexual activity at all, which, in itself, is entirely unnatural. She agreed that it would be better if, while she was here and responding so well and so quickly to treatment that, for the sake of another couple of visits, she should have this treated. So once more she relaxed and we went back to her childhood when her mother was bathing her and as her mother ran her hands between her legs, she told my patient never to let a man touch her there because, "They'll only hurt you." So from those few words all the problems of this lady had arisen. Her unnatural feelings towards sex created a snoring problem and the removal of her snoring problem, by the hypnotist, had created her bed wetting problem.

Symptom removal is NEVER the answer and the tragedy is that the hypnotist involved in this case, like so many others, may genuinely believe that they have helped the patient. He did stop her snoring but in doing so created a far worse problem, particularly for someone sleeping in hotel beds regularly.

One is nervous tension, I should say
was nervous tension, because i'm a much
more relaxed person now. You have

Female Age 42

Dear David,

Just a short note to let you know that after my treatment regarding my fear of dentists, I am now able to receive treatment and have arranged to have all of my front teeth bridged, which means approximately three hours in the dentist chair.

Without your help, this would not be possible and I can only thank you on behalf of my teeth.

Dear Mr. Lesser,

About six weeks ago, I fixed up an appointment with you to combat my smoking habit. That session has proved to be remarkably successful and I am very pleased to report that all desire to smoke has become a thing of the past.

However, at the same time of my initial approach to you, I mentioned briefly that I had a sexual problem - long, on-going, that causes me great worry and distress - my compul

Male Aged 34

Enjoyment is Wrong

"I wasn't hypnotised you know. I heard every word you said". Patiently I explained to her, for the fourth time, that under hypnosis you hear everything. I explained that eighty percent of the people who come for treatment do not feel hypnotised because they have been expecting something dramatic to happen. They have been expecting their minds to go blank, to become unconscious or feel their will being taken over.

Hypnosis, I explained, is simply a state of relaxation. One in which you are fully aware of everything that is said and every background noise.

"......and you were very relaxed, weren't you?" I asked.

"I've never been so relaxed." replied Mrs Meredith, "but I wasn't hypnotised."

I went through the explanations that I always give at least twice during the consultation and once more when I start inducing relaxation with every new patient. But I knew that Mrs Meredith was going to be one of the difficult ones to convince and while I do not usually bother to prove the hypnotic state to people, with her particular personality and problem she really needed to have faith from the start.

I had ten minutes for a cup of coffee before the next patient and decided to sacrifice my refreshment to give Mrs Meredith some hope of relieving her condition. She was getting desperate, she could no longer tolerate sex with her husband and knew her marriage was breaking up. Hypnotherapy was her last resort. Her doctor told her it was a passing phase but it had been getting steadily worse during the last two years of their marriage. Marriage-guidance had been no help, nor had a psychiatrist, and she had even tried accupuncture and faith healing. Hypnotherapy was her last hope as it is with most people who should try hypnotherapy first because it is the only way that the cause of the problem can be found out, instead of just having the symptoms eased temporarily.

I relaxed her back into hypnosis once more and told her to imagine that I was immobilising her left arm by putting straps around her wrist, elbow and upper arm, tying her securely to the chair in which she was lying. It was a beautiful warm summer day and she was wearing a sleeveless dress, so when I told her to try and lift her arm I could watch her muscles straining against the non-existent straps. She really strained against those straps but she could not lift her arm at all.

I heard the door bell ring, so I knew my next patient would be waiting and I took Mrs Meredith out of that state of relaxation and asked her if she now believed she had been hypnotised.

She looked a little puzzled, "I could have lifted my arm if I had really wanted to."

I reminded her of what I had told her during the consultation, that hypnosis only relaxed her conscious mind and let her subconscious come to the fore, that being only a computer, the subconscious could not analyse or criticise what I said and could only accept unless it already contained conflicting information. The conscious mind, however, still listened to my words and being conscious she knew that if she had made the effort she could have used her conscious mind to make her arm lift. Being so relaxed, however, she could not be bothered to bring her conscious mind into play because the situation was not important enough to warrant it.

She began to look a little doubtful, she still did not feel that she had been hypnotised, but she was beginning to wonder.

"I don't want to spend my time and your money doing parlour tricks," I told her as I walked her to the door, "just accept that I can recognise hypnosis, whereas you don't recognise it because you are expecting something comletely different. The important thing is that you accept it. Accept the meaning of the words. As I told you before, the whole basis of this treatment is acceptance by you, so now just accept that you were hypnotised and I'll get rid of your problem for you."

On her next visit, I first of all corrected the last sentence. "I will help you get rid of your problem," I told her, "but you are the one who will actually do it. I'm going to act as your guide, rather like a driving instructor - I can tell you what to do but it is up to you to accept my instructions and act on them. I cannot control you but if you accept my guidance then, together, we can solve your problem."

She had already told me that before she was married she had been 'very sexy' but since marriage she had a steadily diminishing desire for sex with her husband. Soon after marriage she began to find intercourse uncomfortable then painful until she had reached the stage where she could not tolerate it any more. The problem had become very acute over the past few months as her husband had two or three affairs and she was frightened of losing him completely.

She informed me that while they were engaged they had indulged in sex play but only while fully clothed and on three occasions her fiance had brought her to orgasm manually through her clothes. However, since marriage she had developed a strong dislike for this as well as for intercourse and had no inclination to indulge in sex at all, except for self-masturbation.

I relaxed her once again into hypnosis and started questioning to find the reason for the lack of normal sexual reactions. She was a very quick and easy subject and went straight back to an incident in her parents' home at the age of twenty-three, very shortly before their wedding. After her parents had gone to bed she and Martin were alone in the living room, kissing and caressing each other. Both of them reached a very high state of sexual excitement and she wanted to have intercourse. In the past, she had only touched Martin through his trousers but on this occasion he partially undressed her, then took off all his own clothes and for the first time in her life she saw an erect penis. She was frightened by its size and the thought of what it would do to her. At school, some of her friends had shown her some pornographic pictures but those were only fantasy. This was reality and she panicked. She was frightened of something that size penetrating her and immediately lost all inclination for sex. She could not go through with intercourse as both he and she had anticipated.

"Are you still frightened by the thought of penetration?"

"Not any more, but it hurts."

"Is that discomfort caused by your mental tension?"

"Yes."

"Give me, in one word, a reason why you are suffering from that mental tension."

After a long pause, the answer came out: "Guilt."

"Are you guilty because you didn't allow Martin to have full sex with you on the occasion you just told me about?"

"Yes. I should have let him."

"So are you saying that because you didn't let him on that

occasion you feel guilty, and because you are guilty you are not allowing yourself to enjoy sex?"

"Yes."

I had to end the session there but at the end of it we both felt that we had made a lot of progress. On the next occasion that she came for treatment, she told me that she had had sex twice during the week and although she had no enjoyment from it, there had been no discomfort, which she felt was a tremendous leap forward. So after relaxing her once more, I checked that we were talking of the exact incident that caused her problem.

"Is that the true incident that caused your inability to have an orgasm and to enjoy sex?"

"Yes."

"In other words, you have been using your inability to enjoy sex as a punishment to yourself for what happened on that one occasion, while you were engaged?"

"Yes."

"That incident lasted only a few minutes. Don't you think that punishing yourself for the next quarter of a century is sufficient?"

"No."

"Does your husband also deserve punishment?"

"No."

"But don't you realise, that in punishing yourself in this way you are also punishing your husband. The fact that he can't make you enjoy sex almost certainly makes him feel inadequate, which is probably the reason for these affairs that you have told me about. He has to prove to himself that he is still a man. You are punishing yourself by only doing without what you do not desire, but you are punishing your husband in a far worse manner, aren't you?"

She had not looked at it like that. "If you allowed yourself to enjoy sex now, and let's face it, you have been punished long enough for something that was not a deliberate act on your part, you would be giving Martin a tremendous amount of happiness, and isn't this the real reason for your coming here for treatment?"

"Yes."

"You know now why you haven't been allowing yourself to enjoy it. You can see the reason. You can see that if there was any punishment due to you, you've had that over and over again, and all punishment must have a time limit on it, according to how bad the crime. But yours wasn't a crime, it was a panic reaction and you have no need to punish yourself any longer, have you."

"No."

"And after all these years, doesn't Martin deserve his punishment to be ended, because he has no reason at all to be punished."

"Yes."

"So from this time onwards, will you start to enjoy your sex with him?"

"Yes."

Just as Mrs Meredith was leaving, she turned to me and said "I'm actually looking forward to it," and the next time she came she told me that, although she had not achieved an orgasm, she had a lot of satisfaction out of sex since the last treatment and she knew inside herself, that she would be able to get complete fulfilment in the near future, that each session was going to become better and better.

However, she could still not make the first move and it was obvious that because of her previous rejection of sex with her husband, she felt that he might reject her rather than experience a rebuff after sex play had started (and even lack of orgasm could be interpreted as rejection). Unfortunately, this was a thing we could not deal with directly; we would have to have him for treatment to make any direct headway. So the only thing she could do was to be patient and show him that he was able to give her the complete satisfaction he obviously wanted to give and the quicker she became more responsive to him and the bigger her response, the quicker this possibility of rejection would become a thing of the past.

At the next session, she told me that things were 'beautiful', but there was only one possible, tiny thing, I could do for her. Her actual problems of sex and orgasms was solved completely satisfactorily for both her and her husband, but when her husband showed affection by putting an arm around her shoulder, she used to 'freeze' and experience considerable tension. So once more under hypnosis, I took her back to find out the incident behind this. She was a most beautiful and supple subject to deal with and went straight back to the age of 15, walking through some fields with a boy who tried to expose her breasts and was fairly aggressive about his intentions. She became thoroughly frightened and ran home, but she still carried this fear with her.

This was an easy problem to put right. After all, the man who now put his hand on her shoulder - or anywhere else - was certainly not going to harm her. He was the one who now gave her the greatest pleasure of her life so she could accept his actions without any worries or doubts at all about his intentions.

The guilt that was stopping her enjoyment was in relation to her husband only. Masturbation did not involve him and she could allow herself to enjoy it but not masturbation by him nor intercourse. Now, at the age of forty-eight and after twenty-five years of marriage she is at last really enjoying sex. Enjoying it to the full benefit not only of herself but of her husband as well.

Dear David,
I'm writing to thankyou sincerley for changing my life completely with your hypnotherapy treatment from some one who endured sex instead of enjoying it you have caused me to get full satisfaction and really tremendous enjoyment. As you know David I had never once enjoyed sex in the past and suffered it because it was something that men needed. Now I realize that women need it as well. It is the greatest thing that has happened to me, and now I really feel fulfilled It is the greatest sensation ever. I can't thank you

enough, for your help, and if my letter can help any one else to find their true needs then please by all means use it.

Thankyou once again, Yours Sincerley.

Female Age 47

your superb relaxation treatment, I feel a healthier, more relaxed and confident woman.

Female Age 44

Smokers

"You're really asking me to take over your will," I told Mr Franks, a bit sharply. "If somebody could do that to you, not only would you be a zombie, a slave, a robot, but I could save thousands of pounds each year in advertising costs. I'm sure you can understand that if I take over your will it would be a simple matter for me to make you come back and pay for further treatment. I could implant in your mind the desire to return every week for years and years. Yet you are having this treatment free of any additional cost. You know from the person who recommended you to come for treatment that the average person only comes for half a dozen treatments to have their problems solved, and that smokers normally only come once. You stopped smoking for several days, after all these years, without me taking over your will - because that is impossible."

"In fact," I went on, "you restarted smoking of your own free will after several days without any wish to smoke. I did the opposite of taking over your will - I gave you back your free will which you did not have when you came here a few days ago. I helped you get rid of your unnatural compulsion to smoke, the thing that was denying you use of your free will. You left here a few days ago without any craving for cigarettes then you made a definite and conscious decision to have one. You had no compulsion, you had no desire to smoke. You made a definite decision to have one. You were using the free will that you hadn't had for years."

"The other day you left here more or less the same as the day before you had your very first cigarette. Before you had your first one you had no craving for tobacco, you had no desire for it at all. Then you made a decision to try smoking. YOU made that decision, nothing was forcing you. Neither was there anything forcing you last night. You made that decision, you used your free will. I cannot stop you doing that."

Before I had given Mr Franks his treatment I had satisfied myself that this was a genuine desire to give up smoking and not pressure put on him by someone else. He had treatment the previous Thursday morning and had stopped smoking without any difficulty at all until the Wednesday night. He had no desire to smoke at all for almost a week, even in the company of smokers who offered him cigarettes. However, one of his friends at the pub kept on insisting that he should take an offered cigarette and, finally, to shut up his friend he had taken one.

"I didn't want it when I took it. I didn't enjoy it when I lit it and I had only taken two or three puffs at it before I put it out. But having taken the cigarette the next one that my friend insisted on was much easier, and then, of course, I realised that the treatment hadn't worked."

"If you didn't want a cigarette, why did you take it?" I asked, "You had become a non-smoker. Do you know of any non-smokers who accept even one cigarette?" He admitted that other non-smokers WERE non-smokers and agreed that for almost a week he had been one. The thought of having a cigarette had not even come into his mind until his friend became so insistent. "With friends who are prepared to damage your health in that way and make you waste up to £500 a year, you don't need any enemies," I remarked, "Remember what I told you when you first came here? I cannot take over your will. I can take away the desire to smoke, the craving to smoke, which is exactly what I did. I took you back to exactly as you were just before you had your first cigarette. Then you were a non-smoker. Then you made a definite decision to become a smoker just as you did when your friend kept offering you one the other day. So you were a non-smoker. You made a definite decision to accept that cigarette and become a smoker again. I cannot stop you doing that and if you intend to do it again, then you are wasting my time. You told me you didn't enjoy it........" He interrupted:

"No, I definitely didn't. I even felt dizzy."

"So it was just like having your first cigarette again," I remarked. "I want you to think, and then answer me. Did you have any desire to take that cigarette from your friend? Did you have any craving for it at all? Could you, without any difficulty whatsoever apart from the difficulty of shutting him up, have gone without that cigarette?"

He did not stop to think, he replied straight away that he did not want it nor did he enjoy it. So I repeated that all I was doing was taking away the desire to smoke, the craving for a cigarette, that I could not take over his will. Then I relaxed him into hypnosis for the second time.

During this treatment I suggested that if anyone insisted that he have a cigarette he should take it and stub it immediately in the nearest ashtray. That would cure his friend!

When he sat up afterwards, I reinforced my previous comments: "No matter if I make your stomach heave and the cigarettes taste foul, you could still try to smoke. I couldn't stop you, no-one can take over your will. You no longer have a desire to smoke, your craving to smoke has disappeared, you no longer need any will power on your part to be a non-smoker for the rest of your life. But you still have the power to make that decision to smoke. If you do, it will be YOUR decision. If I did make your stomach heave and tobacco taste foul, think of how your first cigarette tasted. That may have made your stomach heave, that almost certainly made you dizzy, but you persevered, you kept on trying until you overcame those feelings, and if you put your mind to it, you can do it again. That is your decision and only YOU can make that decision. I have helped you get into a position where you can make that decision without any unnatural compulsions. You no longer wish to smoke, but I have not taken you over, you still have free will, decisions now rest with you. In taking away that craving I have given you back your free will. How you use it is your concern. You now have no unnatural compulsion to smoke."

Mr Franks is now a confirmed non-smoker, but he reminded me of the first person who came for anti-smoking treatment a long time ago. I had answered the telephone to her myself, and when she wanted to book for a treatment I had offered her an appointment for the following afternoon.

"Can't you do it before then?" She enquired. "I want to do it while my mind is made up."

I told her that the only time before that would be very late that same evening. That was a serious mistake. After smoking twenty a day for many years, would twenty-four hours make that much difference?

Her comment of 'while her mind was made up' really meant that she wanted me to make her mind up for her. She was not serious in her desire to stop. Unfortunately, I was not as wise then as I am now, I would not accept people in that frame of mind now, but I had only just started in practice and was a little naive. The lady came and I spent nearly two hours trying to get her into hypnosis. She just would not accept any suggestion about relaxation. She rejected all of them and I finally had to accept defeat. Before she left, she told me she had met a 'very nice chap' at a disco the night before and he was a non-smoker. She did not really want to give up, but thought he did not like smokers.

Ever since that occasion I have checked every smoker that comes. "Is it your wish to give up smoking, or are you being pushed into it by someone else? I can only help if you really want to stop. It has to be your decision." Once I am satisfied that they do genuinely want to give up smoking, then I will give them treatment and no matter how many they are smoking, they can stop. People smoking from five a day to as many as eighty cigarettes a day will stop without any difficulty at all. The number of cigarettes a day they smoke makes no difference at all. If they want to stop smoking they will accept what I say to them under hypnosis and their desire to smoke will disappear completely.

Smoking is the only problem that can be completely cured in only one session. No other problem can be treated in this way, but there are a small percentage of people that have to come for a follow up treatment like Mr Franks. On the other hand, as I make no additional charge on any follow-up treatments for the first month, there are a few who come when another session is not necessary - like the lady who thought she was not getting her money's worth unless she came for a second treatment, or the one who came the day before the month of free treatment was due to finish. She had not had any desire to smoke at all, but thought that she may as well get in another free treatment 'just in case;' or even people like Mrs Jones, who had been an eighty a day smoker, who gave it up immediately after treatment but rang in a panic two days later and came in for another session. She told me that all her neighbours had known that she was coming for hypnotherapy to give up smoking, and that one teenager had come over to her the day after she had been to see me and had made fun of her.

This girl had said that hypnotherapy does not work, that she had wasted her money, while all the time she was not only smoking in front of her but blowing the smoke into her face. In the end she waved her cigarette under the nose of Mrs Jones and asked if she wanted a puff. Mrs Jones got into a panic and telephoned for another treatment. I asked her if she had enjoyed that puff and she said that just the one puff had made her dizzy. Did she want a cigarette? Did she want to smoke before she took the puff? No. Did she want another cigarette after she had that? No.

Did she feel that she would like a smoke now? No. But she was worried that she would start again. So, I gave her another treatment, but then, about four days later she was once again on the telephone and came up for treatment again. She had been out shopping, caught the bus to come home, there was no room downstairs on the bus (which was the non-smoking part) and she had, therefore, gone upstairs where it was fairly thick with smoke. She thought that by breathing in all the fumes she would be rekindling the desire to smoke. I asked her once more whether she had wanted to smoke while she was on the bus, whether she had wanted to smoke since then or wanted to have a cigarette while she was sitting here talking to me. To all these questions she replied "No." So I said to her, "Think of all the chances you've had. Think of the person who gave you that puff, how she goaded you, how she made fun of you, how she insisted that you did want to smoke. Think of that situation on the bus and yet you still have had no desire to smoke since the first time you came here.

"I did what I said I would do. I helped you to become a non-smoker again. You don't need any more treatment, you are a confirmed non-smoker, you obviously will have no desire ever to smoke again. You don't need the third treatment."

"The offer still holds. For the price of the first treatment, you get as many treatments during the next month as you may need, but you do not need one now, it is not necessary. By all means, telephone if you wish to, anytime during the rest of this month, and I will give you treatment if you need it, but I know that it is not necessary and I think that you know that it is not necessary, too, don't you?" She agreed with me and four months later, she recommended another lady for treatment, who told me that Mrs Jones had not wanted to smoke, had not had a cigarette, and was very, very happy indeed. Mrs Jones had persuaded this lady to come by saying how much fitter she felt and that her head and her breathing were so much clearer. Mrs Jones had saved the cost of her treatment in only one week because of the large amount that she was smoking. The average person will save the cost of their treatment in less than a month, yet there are still people who are not prepared to spend a little money to stop smoking. There are also the people who use their therapist as an excuse and have no intention to give up. They return to their family saying "I've tried Hypnotherapy, it doesn't work so leave me alone to smoke in peace," and those with the attitude "he couldn't take me over" quite ignoring the fact that, above all, Hypnotherapy requires acceptance by the patient.

That is why I always ask "Is it your decision to give up?" and this is the most important question. A Hypnotherapist can only do what the patient wants him to do. Anything else, the patient will automatically reject. No matter how good that Hypnotherapist is, he cannot take over the will of anyone else at all, he can only work WITH them to achieve what they desire.

Wolverhampton.

Had your treatment on 1st Sept, So grateful to you for curing US of smoking. Good wishes for 1984

Male and Female Mid 30's

nearly a month now since I had a cigarette and I dont ever feel or bother about them

Female Aged 25

"I Heard Every Word"

"I heard every word", is probably the most usual comment that a hypnotherapist hears. No matter how much you explain before hand what the state of hypnosis is and how people will react, they never really believe you. A good example of this was a man who came with his wife, both of them wishing to give up smoking. As I have mentioned in a previous chapter, smokers normally only need one session and this is the only problem one can deal with in a single treatment.

They had their treatment and left and I heard nothing from them for about eight months when the lady came back with a friend of hers, who also wanted to give up smoking. Before taking the new lady into the consulting room, I had a word in the reception with her friend, who was telling me that since she had come to me and given up smoking, her breathing was much easier and she felt much more energetic. I then asked her how her husband was and she said:

"I have often wanted to ring you up and tell you because it is really so funny. When you had finished us that night, we walked out of the building and as we stood on the pavement, my husband turned to me and said 'That was a bloody waste of money'. But you know - he's never smoked since!"

The man had been trying desperately to give up as he was a diabetic and his doctor has been putting a lot of pressure on him but he had been unable to stop smoking up to the day that he came for treatment and had never smoked since. It may seem peculiar that he did not believe that he was hypnotised but to this day he still does not really believe it. It is quite possible that he thinks of it as a coincidence that he was able to give up the very day he had treatment. Yet I know, from watching his reactions, that he was in a good state of relaxation and that it was the hypnosis that enabled him to stop smoking.

It seems peculiar to people that they can lie back in a chair being conscious of every word that is said to them and yet have those words alter their lives so completely. There are many people who have been cured of serious problems and never believed that they have been hynotised. One of these was a lady who came to lose weight. It is almost unbelievable when you are working with someone, how they can go so easily and so deeply into relaxation and respond exactly as you wish them to, and still not believe that they have been hypnotised.

The very first time we started to find out why this particular lady was overweight, she went straight back to the age of five. She was on a swing in the barn at her grandmother's farm. Her cousin was pushing her and she was going higher and higher on that swing until she let go and fell to the floor. She woke up in her grandmother's living room, lying on the sofa with her grandmother bending over her and her words were "It should have been mum".

The fact that mother was not there started the feeling that her mother did not want to be there, and thus she experienced rejection. Rejection is one of the most common reasons why women put on weight.

As with every other problem, the explanation is a logical one. You have to go back to the moment a baby is born. When it is picked up and fed, it is given love at the same time. A baby cannot analyse, it knows it gets a feeling of comfort from the mixture of love and food, but has no idea which part of that mixture is actually giving it that comfort. So far as the baby is concerned it gets conditioned into expecting both love and food as requirements for its comfort, and the moment it loses part of that package - the love - it feels discomfort. Because it cannot replace the love, it will turn to the part of the package that is available - it will turn to food as a replacement for that love.

This rejection does not have to be true rejection, imagined rejection is enough. If someone imagines it then that is their belief, that is the truth to them, as in the case of this lady. Her mother was not there when she was hurt. Her mother was not there when she was badly needed, and she felt rejection. The feeling in her case may have been only short lived because at five years old, she was old enough to realise that her mother was at work when she fell off the swing. She may not have realised how long she had been lying there but she must have come to realise that shortly after she regained consciousness. The damage, however, had already been done; the feeling of rejection had started a new programme in her computer and she turned to food.

This lady had no memory of this incident before she recalled it under hypnosis, and she had to check the validity of the memory with her mother. In spite of the ability to recall a memory that had been completely lost from her conscious mind and in spite of the tremendous change in her desire for food, she never once believed that she was under hypnosis. At the end of the treatments, when she

told me that she did not feel that she had been hyp
her that she was very relaxed. Her reply was, "I ha
relaxed in my life before: but I wasn't hypnotised".
spent in explanation of hypnosis is, in most cases,
People still feel that something dramatic should hap
should be taken over in some way, that everything sho ... black, or that they should feel my mind groping around inside theirs. Hypnosis is only a state of relaxation, a state that everybody goes through twice a day - immediately before they go to sleep at night and once again as they come out of sleep into wakefulness in the morning. At night they drift from being fully alert through various stages of relaxation into the stage of hypnosis and through that into natural sleep. They know that nothing dramatic happens then, that in most cases they do not even know what sort of state they are in. They only realise that they have been asleep when they wake up again. Yet is is difficult to accept that they can be guided part of the way into sleep, and in that state achieve cures that sometimes seem almost miraculous, without something dramatic happening. Nobody stops to think that drama would normally destroy relaxation, they are opposites.

One of the other phrases commonly used by patients is, "You are my last resort". A hypnotherapist is usually last on their list. We get people whom nobody else has been able to cure, people who have been to their doctors, their osteopaths and acupuncturists, they may have been through the hands of the psychiatrist, tried self-medication from the health food shop, even had spiritual-healing or faith-healing or any of the multitude of therapies that now seem to be springing up. Yet, hypnotherapy is the logical treatment, it is based completely on logic. One has to admit that one does not fully understand hypnosis itself, but having accepted the fact that we can achieve hypnosis, the actual treatment of patients is pure logic. One of the ladies who used the words that I was 'her last resort' was someone who had suffered from agoraphobia for ten years. When she went outside she not only felt frightened, she had a very big increase in her heartbeat and she felt her head reeling. On bad days she had to keep to just one room of her house with the curtains drawn and unable even to answer the telephone because it was connected to the outside world. She only needed two treatments to cure her and I had a postcard from her a month or two after the treatment which she had posted at a seaside resort having gone on holiday with her family for the first time in ten years. Her problem was logical and we used logic to cure it. At ge of twenty-five, when she was unmarried, she had a ughter. She wanted to leave her home and her mother told her that she might as well leave as she would just make as big a mess of her life if she left home as she would if she stayed there. Her father, on the other hand, told her not to leave. He said that they wanted to look after her, that she would be safe with them.

Her interpretation was that there was danger outside the home and as she left home shortly after the conversation with her parents, anything at all that went wrong, even such small things as missing the bus when she had to get somewhere on time, she translated into 'making a mess of things'. She translated other things into danger outside and although she is now married and has two additional children, she gradually built up everything that happened outside the home in a negative way, and added them on to that computer programme she had started at the age of twenty-five until, a few years later, she had developed agoraphobia and had suffered it all those years since then. The agoraphobia had led her into depression. The psychiatrist had given her abreaction, an unpleasant sensation that rarely produces results, but it only took a couple of treatments to find out and correct the cause. What a shame that a pleasant, bright woman like her had had to suffer for ten years for the sake of about an hour and a half's actual treatment, which was all it took to put it right. She could only come for treatment on what was a 'good day' and even then she had to come by taxi with a taxi-driver who was known to her and with her head covered in a blanket so that she would not have to look at the outside world. She never took the blanket off until she was inside our reception. If she had done so she knew she would 'pass out'.

There is a third very common expression used by patients, early in the consultation. Many of them will say 'I know what has caused it'. I always listen politely, but never believingly, because I have never come across a case yet where somebody actually knew the cause of their problem. To know the cause means that they must logically understand the path from the cause to the effect that it is now having on them. If they can logically understand it then, logically, they will correct it. Automatically, they will put it right. One lady who said she knew the cause was a lady who came with a fear of birds.

She was frightened of any bird, a large one, a small one, a live one or a dead one; even a picture of a bird in a magazine was enough to create that fear. She was a very pleasant looking woman, with a nice personality, plenty of common-sense and the last sort of person you would think who would have any sort of problem at all. She came in to ask for details of hypnotherapy and as I was free at the time, I had a few minutes chat with her in the reception and she told me that she knew the cause of her fear. Her grandmother used to own a farm which she visited regularly and at four years old she had gone to the barn one day, pulled the door open to go in and, as she did so, three dead chickens, which were hanging on the back of the barn door, swung towards her and frightened her. To a child of four, that would have been frightening. Her explanation of the cause seemed fairly sound but the real reason for her fear of birds went back to when she was three years old. She was in the pushchair on the pier at the seaside and her mother was talking to a stranger who was telling her of a report in the paper about a bird that had flown into a pram which had its hood up and had apparently panicked and pecked at the child's eyes. That was the root of her fear of birds. This was another lady who had no memory of the incident before and she also checked with her mother about the truth of it. Her mother was amazed that she had recalled the incident and said to her, "I never thought that you would remember that because you never asked anything about it, you never said anything at all and you were such an inquisitive child".

It was a coincidence that the animals hanging on the barn door were also birds. That had stuck in her memory because she used to feed those birds and she regarded them as friends. She was shaken when she saw them hanging dead on the door, but that caused sadness not fear, and her fear was a real one. When she came here, it was shortly after a new butcher had opened on the main shopping street near her and her words to me were that it had cut her shopping area down by half. She could not go anywhere near that butcher's shop because it had birds hanging up in it. She used to have to cross the road before she got near the butcher's shop and recross long after she had passed it. There were about fourteen shops in a row that she could no longer visit. Since the cause has been found out, since she understands how the fear was caused logically, she used her own logic to correct it, and has actually gone into the same butcher to buy her meat.

Dear David,
This letter is to thank you for all the help you gave my mother when she was suffering very badly from Tension, Depression & Anxiety, you should see her now her improvement is unbelievable she has got rid of her depression completly & now she is in the frame of mind to look forward instead of back..........
as I have said she is very determined now to help herself, had we come to you first I am sure my Mum would never have needed any Drugs whatsever. Thank you. Yours Sincerley

Patient: Female Age 76

Dear sir
I think you have helped me. Before I was not geting eney work done but now I am finishing me work.
I have a lot of engey and when I come and see you I use my imaginasion. In school I work harder and when

My mom and dad
went to perenson eving
the teatchers thunk I
have inproved. Thank
you very much for
helping me.

Yours gratfully

Male Age 10

Fear of Flying

"Imagine that you are ill; imagine that you've got some sort of virus or germ in your body. Imagine that you've gone to the doctor and been prescribed a medicine which will kill that virus. You start to take the medicine as instructed three times a day and by the time you have got half way down the bottle, the medicine has weakened the virus to such an extent that you are feeling a lot better, and because you feel better you stop taking the medicine. That virus is still alive in your body, weakened, but alive, and without being continually dosed with the medicine it can recover from the effects of the dosage you have already taken. Gradually, it gathers strength once more and begins to multiply until you are back again as ill as you were before."

"This is exactly the same with hypnosis. The person you went to the first time to cure your depression only tried to treat your symptoms. This was effective to some extent, and you started to feel better. You felt a lot better, and when you stopped having treatment from that hypnotist both you and she felt the treatment had been a success. However, she had made no attempt to find out and put right the cause of your problem. The reason for your depression was still there, and because it was a reason, a very logical reason, it gradually wore away at the effects of the hypnosis and gradually you started to slide back again into your depression."

"Now, I too am going to treat your symptoms, but symptom treating is a very minor part of what is going to happen here. In fact, you can be cured without having your symptoms treated at all. I am going to find out the reason why you have this depression, and having found it out, we shall correct the cause. You could, therefore, lose your depression without any symptom treatment at all although treating them will speed up getting rid of the last of the effects."

I cleared up Lorna's depression in approximately three-quarters of the total number of treatments she had eighteen months before from the hypnotist she had gone to. At the last session she was bubbling over, but had a further problem for which she wanted help. Both she and her husband had very good jobs and, as they were unable to have any children, they were in the position where they could enjoy life and be able to take three or four holidays abroad every year. However, she had a terrible fear of flying. Over the last two or three years she had screwed up her courage sufficiently to go abroad once every year with her husband, but she had to be sedated before the trip and be supported onto the plane by her husband.

Having experienced curative hypnotherapy for her depression and understanding how her mind gives apparently unreasoned reactions she believed that I could help. She knew the reaction was a ridiculous one. She had first flown when she was sixteen without any unnatural apprehension and she had made many trips by air between that age and the age of thirty, but in the following six years she had developed a terror of going on a plane. Under hypnosis first of all she took me back to the age of thirty.

"Did something unpleasant happen to you?"

"No"

"Has your fear of flying been caused by something that someone said?"

"Yes"

"Was it a man?"

"Yes"

"Was it a relative of yours?"

"No"

"A friend?"

"No"

"Was it someone known to you?"

"No"

"Were the words said directly to you?"

"No"

"Were they words that you overheard?"

"No"

"Was the person a stranger to you?"

"No"

It is amazing how literal the mind can be. We had a situation here of a man whose words had caused her problem. The man was not a stranger yet was not known to her. The words he had said were not said to her, neither had she overheard them - two rather puzzling apparent contradictions. She refused to actually recall the words into her memory and tell me about them because of the unwelcome emotions it was likely to arouse. So I was in rather an awkward situation being unable to find out the exact words, unable to find out who had said them or how she had heard them. At the next session we tried a different attack, filling in background first and it gradually emerged that the words she had heard which had caused her fear of flying were said in her own home, but the person who said them was not there at the time.

We seemed to be getting deeper into inexplicable territory until by various methods it suddenly came out that it was a newscaster on the television. So everything that she had said that seemed contradictory, dropped into place. The newscaster was not in her home at the time; he had not been talking directly to her neither had she overheard. She had been sitting, watching and listening; the man was not a stranger to her as she had seen him many times on the television, but neither was he personally known to her. It had been unfortunate that we had wasted a little time in that Lorna would not visualise the event because if she visualised it, she would have actually heard the words that she did not want to hear. I had been forced to fall back onto the 'Yes/No'method of questioning. Continuing with this method it turned out that the newscaster was talking about a plane crash. He did not know why it had crashed and he talked about people having their backs broken and the plane having its back broken.

"Was this the first plane crash that you had heard announced on television?"

"No"

"Was there something particular in this broadcast?"

"Yes"

Naturally, I thought it was the announcement about the people having their backs broken, but it was not. Nor was it that the plane had broken its back. It turned out to be that the announcer had said that the cause of the crash "was not known".

Usually, when announcing a plane crash the newscaster would use words to the effect that the 'black box' - the flight recorder - was being sought to find out the cause of the crash. Or he might say, "The cause of the crash is not YET known". However, in this particular case he had used the words "The cause of the crash is not known". He had left out those three little letters 'Y-E-T' and her interpretation of that was not just that the cause was not known but that the cause would never be known.

"Did you develop your fear of flying following this news broadcast because of some previous information?"

"Yes"

"Was this previous information something you had read?"

"No"

"Was it something you had seen?"

"No"

"Something you had heard?"

"Yes"

"Something that was said to you in person?"

"Yes"

Now we were on the track of it. We knew when she first had the unnatural reaction but we were now going to find out why she had reacted unnaturally and she took me back to the age of three. She was with her mother in the garden when a plane had flown overhead. Her mother looked up and said, "If we were meant to fly we would have been born with wings".

As Lorna herself said afterwards, it is all so ridiculously simple. She had stored in her subconscious mind the reason why that plane had crashed. She was probably the only person, out of all the millions in the country who had heard that same broadcast, who knew the reason why that plane had crashed. Human beings were not meant to fly in the first place according to her mother, and at three years old when her mother used those words, her mother was infallible.

In view of Lorna's personality, I could not resist curing her with a bit of ridicule.

"When you were three years old, did your mother go out shopping?"

"Yes"

"Did she go shopping in the nude?"

"No"

"If your mother really believed that we should only use what we are born with, then if we were meant to wear clothes surely we would have been born with them?"

I got no reply to this, so asked her, "Did your mother ever go on a bus?"

"Yes"

"Surely, if we were meant to have wheeled transport, we would have been given wheels instead of feet, wouldn't we?"

She lay there without answering in any way at all but a big smile spread over her face and I knew that she had corrected the impression given to her by her mother's words.

I finished her treatment on August 10th and she was flying on holiday on the eleventh. By the skin of our teeth, we had cured her in time, and when she sat up after this treatment, I said to her:

"You are really going to enjoy this holiday aren't you?"

"I hope so"

"You know so," I said, "but you haven't yet proved it. All you have to do now is prove it to yourself.

And a few weeks later I received the following letter

Dear David,

I would like to thank you for helping me to overcome my fear of flying.

I found that not only was I more relaxed on my outward journey - . - - . - . - . - - - - - - - .

I also ate & drank my meals and went in to the cock-pit with the pilot and belive me that is 100% inprovement as on past flights I have not even moved out of my seat. Once again many thanks.

Yours Sincerley

Female Age 38

Some months later she came to our allied clinic for treatment and I spent ten minutes chatting to her. She told me that she had had a fair amount of tension as she got on the plane but had taken no sedatives or tranquilizers and during the flight she had gradually relaxed. She had had a good holiday and had not bothered to use the special tape that I had given her and which she had taken with her together with a personal tape-recorder. I had felt that this may have been an asset in view of the fact that there had been so little time between correcting her reaction and her actual flight. She said that by the end of the flight out to her holiday destination, she knew that the fear was behind her forever. There had been virtually no tension on the flight home and she was looking forward to another holiday they had booked in Crete.

It is all a question of interpretation. Millions of people may have seen that same news broadcast, but almost certainly only one reacted as she did because of the particular information that was put there at an age when she was too young to analyse and correct, and therefore allowed it to take root and to flourish until that newscaster caused the fear to bloom.

Dear David
I'd just like to thankyou for the way in which your treatment has helped me, by giving me confidence in driving. Now that I understand why I was so nervous of driving I can now go out and learn properly like everyone else. I've put in for my test. I'll let you know when I pass!

Thanks again

Sue

Female Age 25

Later she sent a note:

Dear David

I *passed* my test !!!

Thanks for all your help

Acceptance

Much of the apprehension about being hypnotised is caused by stage hypnotists. Many people have a fear that I am likely to make them do silly tricks and that I am going to completely take them over as this appears to be what happens at a public entertainment.

Stage hypnotists, however good they may be, can only work with under 2% of the population. The audience does not realise how the people influenced by the hypnotist will only go along with his suggestions as far as they really want to. There is no way that the hypnotist can cause a person to do anything against their wish.

One has only to watch one of these showmen giving instructions to two women, telling them that they are dressed in a grass skirt and are going to do a hula-dance, and watch how those ladies interpret the dance to realise that they are interpreting it in their own way. They are prepared only to accept the instructions that they wish to accept. They both heard exactly the same words because he instructed them both at the same time but the extroverted one will do a very sexy routine, whereas the more shy of the two will hardly move her hips at all. They react as they would if they were not under hypnosis. One of those ladies may feel that she does not want to make a fool of herself in that way but she is in the situation where she is on the stage and a multitude of eyes are watching her. To refuse to do anything would probably make her look more foolish than doing a little, so she makes tiny little movements to keep the hypnotist happy and not make her feel like an idiot. She brings into play her own likes, her own dislikes, her own moral standards and in every way interprets what the hypnotist says to her in the light of her own personality and character.

There are a few stage-hypnotists who are very entertaining but having made that comment, I must make it plain that I am wholeheartedly against public performances of this nature. The hypnotist is a showman not a therapist. His whole attention is devoted to entertaining an audience, and he pays little attention or care to the people under hypnosis. It is rather like being entertained by a surgeon doing a leg-amputation on a music hall stage. Making a leg-amputation into an entertainment and ensuring first of all that the audience are kept amused rather than putting his whole attention on his patient. In fact, I will take this a stage further. If a surgeon was doing a leg-amputation for entertainment purposes he would at least be a qualified surgeon, whereas a hypnotist does not know with what he is dealing. It is more like the local butcher doing an amputation in public. After all the butcher probably does more cutting up and carving of bodies than a surgeon ever does, and there is a tremendous similarity between the bodies of animals and the bodies of humans. But who would entrust themselves to a butcher for surgery?

The biggest danger with stage-hypnotists is that they do not realise the problems they can cause. They do their show, they pack up and go home and sometimes (often a very considerable time afterwards) a problem that they have caused has shown up. For instance, a popular trick with stage hypnotists is to make a person become so rigid that they can be placed over the back of two chairs, with their neck on the back of one and their ankles on the back of another and no support in between. The hypnotist will then invite maybe two or three people from the audience to sit on that unsupported body without doing any sort of checks to begin with whether that person is strong enough to support all that weight without any damage. When he takes the person out of hynosis he tells them that they are going to 'wake up' feeling fine and good, which is a suggestion which is obviously acceptable to his guinea pig. Therefore it may be days or even weeks later when that person starts to have back problems by which time, of course, he no longer associates the problems with the hypnotist, and the hypnotist himself has no idea of the trouble he left behind him after his show.

A stage hypnotist, like a hypnotherapist, is dealing with words, but while he is talking to the person under hypnosis, his main attention is directed at the audience as they are the ones who are paying for the exhibition. He takes little care of the people he should be really concentrating on; he is only interested in the public's reactions. Sometimes a hypnotist does not fully cancel the suggestions given. For instance, a suggestion may be given that there is no feeling at all in one leg, and if this is accepted by the person under hypnosis, all sensation will go completely from that limb. If the suggestion is not fully cancelled, it could happen that a couple of days later that person was sitting with their legs crossed and they experienced some loss of sensation because they had been in one position too long. They could then translate that loss of sensation into loss of all sensation because of the suggestions which had not been completely nullified, and they could experience a type of paralysis in that limb for a period.

Naturally, this sort of thing cannot occur with a properly qualified hypnotherapist who is dealing with one individual without any outside distractions, and who will make sure that any suggestions given are only beneficial suggestions and would take all the necessary precautions.

Stage hypnotists, of course, can only work with a very small percentage of the population. Their method is simple but very effective. Many people ask about stage hypnotists at a consultation. Basically, these showmen are divided into three different types: There is the complete charlatan, who uses stooges in the audience and does not use hynosis at all. There is the man who does use hypnosis but takes people behind the scenes for a long time before the show starts so that they know what is expected of them once the audience is watching; and there is the genuine stage hypnotist (and in using the word 'genuine' I must make plain that I am more strongly against these people than the other two, because they are the dangerous ones). The genuine hypnotist will make suggestions to the audience, possibly something along the lines of asking them to put their hands together and they will find that they are unable to take them apart. Between one and two percent of the audience will respond to this and the entertainer will then ask them to come up onto the stage and he will release their hands for them. He then has on the stage the small percentage of the audience which is very receptive. He works with them for a few minutes but will then, almost certainly, send back into the audience a few of those who he concludes do not have the other qualities, apart from susceptibility, that he needs. What he is really looking for are people who have always wanted the opportunity of getting on a stage and doing something, but have lacked the chance or the confidence to do it. Now they are prepared to do it because, even if the audience laugh at them when they make fools of themselves, in their own minds they will be putting the blame on the hypnotist.

The similarity between a stage hypnotist and a hypnotherapist is roughly the same as between the butcher and the surgeon that I mentioned before. They may use the same basic tool, but it is not the tool that has the skill, it is the person using it. The showmen will never make good hypotherapists because all the time they are concerned with the impression they are making rather than curing their patient.

Much of the blame for people being frightened of having hypnotherapy to cure their problems lies squarely on the shoulders of the stage hypnotist. People in an audience, watching those on the stage making fools of themselves, believe that they have been taken over. They believe that the showman has taken complete control whereas this is an absolute impossibility. He is working with people who are prepared to go along with his suggestions and this, of course, is the secret of hypnosis - acceptance of suggestions. Even under deepest hypnosis, people will only accept what they are prepared to accept which is why a stage hypnotist will often send back into the audience some of the most easily hypnotised people in the country and why a hypnotherapist is always careful about what he asks a patient to accept. A hypnotherapist is only interested in curing the patient; he is not interested in an audience or in demonstrating how clever he is.

Occasionally one gets a patient who starts with the words, "My doctor does hypnosis, but he couldn't hypnotise me and he says that I am one of the ten or twenty percent of the population who cannot be hypnotised". The fact that these people have come to a proper hypnotherapist shows that they have not fully accepted their doctor's suggestions that they are not able to be sufficiently relaxed for treatment, and just like anyone else, they can be relaxed into hypnosis as easily as people who have a strong belief that they are good subjects.

Other people who have accepted hypnosis easily elsewhere sometimes tell me that the person who hypnotised them before has implanted a post-hypnotic suggestion that no-one else will ever be able to hypnotise them, but, after a few minutes talk with these people, they go into hypnosis as easily as anyone else. Once they have accepted the idea that no-one can give them this sort of instruction against their will (and it is obviously against their will or they would not be coming to me for treatment) then they will accept the suggestions necessary to take them into the beautiful state of relaxation called hypnosis. There is no-one who cannot be hypnotised. There are people who will not be hypnotised and there are people who are unacceptable as hypnotists to certain individuals. One needs to be able to trust the therapist. One does not have to like them, but trust is a necessity at least for the first time of hypnosis when apprehension is at its greatest.

With luck on my side, the
exam was moved from 6/11
– 26/11. So I had 3 weeks
of hard study. I have never
read so much. What's more
I enjoyed it Funny!

I feel a strange air
of confidence with regards
to passing the Exam.

There were 3 papers, each 2hrs
long. I think I have just
passed in each one. I tried
to do in 3 weeks what
everyone else does in 10 months
or thereabouts.

So, I now await my Results
in Feb: 85. I'll let you
know if I pass

Thanking You.

Female Age 28

Dear Mr Lesser,
I am writing to let you know that I am now feeling alot better as my headaches have now completely gone.

Male Age 14

Mummy Knows Best

Dorothy was a charming and highly intelligent 62 year old lady who came to have help to reduce her weight. She knew a tremendous amount about computers as this was part of her job. She quickly understood my explanations on the workings of the human computer, although I feel that she had difficulty in believing that she was carrying around a computer with her which could influence her and make her overeat against her wishes and against her better judgement.

She had suffered two heart attacks and quite apart from wishing to improve her appearance, was worried that the excess weight she was carrying was obviously putting an additional strain on her heart. I explained to her that her compulsion to overeat - or to eat for 'comfort' - which she recognised as being completely uncontrollable by her, was caused by some incorrect information in her computer; that the only possible way that one can get an incorrect answer from a computer is if someone puts in incorrect information. That there is no such thing as computer error, it is always human error. She understood this but she did not, however, believe that she was 'computer controlled'. I pointed out to her that this need for excessive food was not a physical need - if it had been then she would be using the food, burning it up instead of storing it in the form of fat around her body. Moreover, it was not a conscious need. Consciously she not only wanted to get rid of her fat for the sake of her appearance and her health but she was even prepared to pay good money to me to help her to get rid of her fat. So if it was not a physical need nor a conscious need...."Where does the compulsion to overeat come from?" I asked her.

"I don't know," she replied, "I can't understand it."

"OK," I said, "just assume for a moment that you are controlled by a computer, in the way that I have suggested. Your conscious mind is the decision making part of your mind, the part that analyses what goes on. It criticises, it refers to the memory banks of your computer as to what happened in similar circmstances in the past. Then it makes the decisions. It is your conscious mind that makes the decision, analyses and makes decisions. There are so many things that go on in your body that are not controlled by your conscious mind. You know that every muscle in your body works when the brain sends an electric impulse down the nerves and you know that that is the only thing that does make a muscle work, don't you?"

"Yes?" she replied questioningly. She looked puzzled.

"You know that your heart is a muscle as well, don't you? And you know that you are not sitting there telling your heart to beat. It is still getting that impulse from your brain, but it isn't the conscious part of your brain that is controlling your heart beat - it's that automatic part of your brain that I am talking about - your subconscious".

"I'm with you so far." She said.

"Right. While we are talking about muscles," I went on "think about picking up a cup. Can you pick up a cup just using your conscious mind?"

"Of course," she said. "I consciously make the decision to pick it up, I consciously move my arm, I consciously grip the cup and consciously lift it up".

"You don't." I told her, "You consciously make the decision. There I agree with you. But having made that decision you then use your subconscious to go through all the actions. Have you any idea how many muscles you have to use to lift that cup, - to lift your arm, to stretch it out, to open your fingers, to close them around the cup and so on? Do you use 10 muscles? 20 muscles? 30? 40? You use the muscles of your shoulder, the elbow, the wrist and fourteen separate joints of the fingers to make them curve around the cup. Each muscle has to be accurately controlled so that you don't lift your arm too high, or grip the cup too hard if it is a plastic one out of a vending machine, nor too lightly if it is a heavy earthenware one which would slip out of your fingers".

"Every movement must also be done in the correct sequence - there is no use closing your fingers before they have reached the cup, and, if your arm movement isn't controlled, you will knock the cup flying. There is no way that you can think your way through each individual muscle. The coffee in that cup would be cold long before your hand reached it!"

"Every move has to be done in the right sequence, at the right speed and with precisely the correct amount of movement. Then the whole process has to be reversed using different muscles to get the cup to your lips. You don't think about any of this. All you do is make the conscious decision to pick up the cup. Everything else you do automatically. You don't even know how many muscles you move. You leave that to your computer, that tremendously efficient part of your mind, your sub-conscious. That is the part that actually moves your muscles. All you do is make the decision because you have analysed and decided you are thirsty."

By now Dorothy was going along with me, she was agreeing.

"Now," I said, "let's go a step further. Have you ever raised your arm to ward off a blow from a falling object? Did you stop to think, to analyse your best move? To wonder whether you'd be better to try jumping out of the way, to lift your arm or turn your body to take the blow on a less painful spot? Had you stopped to work it out you would have been hit before your decision was made. So your automatic reflexes came into play. The automatic part of your mind took over to protect you. All those many muscles did their individual jobs without any conscious thought. Your sub-conscious reacted to do its job which is your protection."

"Maybe you only imagined that object was going to fall, yet you still reacted in the same way. Due to that mis-information in your imagination, your computer reacted for your protection."

"I know the feeling," she said, "but what sort of wrong information could be in my computer to make me overeat and how could over-eating protect me?"

"Shall we use the word mis-interpretation?" I asked. "Because this is the real word that lies at the root of your problem. It is your computer that tells you when you are hungry, when you need food. You only physically need food when your energy stores are getting low. Then your sub-conscious, which monitors and controls all bodily systems, causes that feeling of hunger so that you eat to replenish your fuel supplies. Mis-information in that computer will cause it to make you feel that you need food when you have no physical need for it at all. Such mis-information is caused by a mis-interpretation of something and with your co-operation we are going to go back to find out what that mis-interpretation is, and because it is a mis-interpretation we can correct it. We can put it right once we know exactly what it is".

"But supposing there is no mis-interpretation?"

"You are the computer expert," I replied "and you know that there is really no such thing as computer error. If you get an electricity bill for several thousand pounds and you 'phone the electricity board to complain, they may tell you that there is a computer error but you are well aware that this is really human error. Someone has put in the wrong information. It will turn out exactly the same with your computer. You have mis-interpreted something that has happened in the past and we can correct it. Are you ready to start?"

"That's what I came for," she said and we then reclined the chair she was sitting on and she followed my words which took her into that very pleasant state of relaxation which we call hypnosis. This is all I do when people come for a consultation. I just show them what it feels like to be in hypnosis so that when they come again they know that all it consists of is a truly beautiful feeling of relaxation. All their apprehension will have gone the second time they come and they will know that this wonderful sensation does not give anyone control over them. They know that they will remain fully conscious, fully in control of themselves and can reject any suggestions made or refuse to answer any question asked. I know that the next time they come they will be looking forward to re-experiencing that feeling once more and have no worries about 'being taken over'.

Dorothy had been 12 stone 12 lbs (180 lbs) on her first visit and on her second visit was just 1 lb lighter. I told her we were going to start the process of finding out the cause of her overeating, and after relaxing her, I got her to visualise what lay at the root of the problem. She took me back to when she was 50 years old, happily working with her colleagues around her. She was happy as she got on with her job, so I said:

"Something must have happened to change your mood. Go forward a few minutes until something happens to change your mood and tell me what is is."

She began to breathe in a laboured manner, then said "Pain!! Pain!!"

I told her she was only visualising the event and not reliving it. That she was not actually re-experiencing the pain, and gradually her breathing subsided to normal.

"It was a terrible pain," She said.

"Was that your heart attack?" I asked her.

"Yes."

I questioned her about the connection between her heart attack and overeating as the first thing anyone is told after a heart attack is to lose any excess weight to reduce strain on the heart. It seemed a most peculiar reaction for her to eat and put on weight as a result of this attack.

"Was it because of the pain that you started overeating?"

"Yes."

"Would any pain cause you to overeat?"

"If it was bad enough."

"Are you telling me that food prevents or lessens pain?"

"Yes."

Puzzling, fascinating, but unfortunately we had reached the end of our time and my next patient was waiting so I had to send her away with an appointment for the following week.

On the next occasion she had lost no more weight but this did not worry me as I knew we were well on the track of her problem and the solution was very near.

After she had relaxed on this occasion I re-commenced the questioning:

"Last time you were here you told me that food prevented or lessened pain. Is this why you overeat? To prevent a recurrence of the pain you experienced when you had that heart attack?"

"Yes."

"Can you tell me how you have come to this conclusion?"

"I don't know."

"Has the idea originated from something you read?"

"No."

"Was it something someone said either directly to you or in your hearing?"

"Someone told me."

"You must go back, Dorothy," I told her, "Go back to the actual incident when this information was given to you. You are now going to visualise the actual incident, you are going to see exactly how you got this idea, and you are going to hear again the exact words that were used. I need to know the precise words that were used and the exact circumstances in which they were spoken. Go back, go back in time and see that incident, hear the exact words because somewhere in those words there is something that you have mis-interpreted. Tell me the exact words."

She lay back in her chair for nearly half a minute. Then she said: "You must eat. Mummy knows best. It will take the pain away. It will make you better."

I asked her how old she was when these words were said to her and she told me she was twelve.

"You were ill at the time, were you?" I queried.

"Diphtheria, very, very ill"

She went on to tell me how her mother was trying to persuade her to eat to build up her strength. Her mother was the source of her learning. Her word was law to Dorothy and she had taken those words literally - overeating would take the pain away and make her better. When that pain, that terrible pain of her heart attack had suddenly struck her, her sub-conscious had reacted by putting into effect those words to protect her from another attack. Without any idea why she was reacting in this way her sub-conscious had made her hungry almost all the time to prevent the pain recurring. She had completely forgotten those words in her conscious. But the sub-conscious never forgets!

Naturally, in this case it was easy to re-interpret her mother's words. Her sub-conscious was logical and could see the illogicality of the reaction. She understood those words used by her mother referred only to the discomfort she was experiencing at the time and not to subsequent illness or pain.

Dorothy had reacted to the excruciating pain of her first heart attack by overeating and putting on weight. Her second attack was less severe and this reinforced the belief - it was less painful because she had been overeating. She therefore ate even more, and the fact that for the last ten years she had no further heart problem had made the reaction even stronger. Now, however, she is her correct weight, a lively and energetic 63 year old, still working hard, enjoying every minute of her life and looking far better than when we first met.

and have shed a stone, I'm sure hypnotherapy sessions I had have helped me conquer my appetite.

Thanking You.

Female Age 28

Dear David,

I am absolultey delighted with the results I have had from reciving treatment at the hynotherapy center for my weight problem and resulting deppresion and lack of Self confedence.

I have already lost over a Stone and I am still redueing without any effort at all, its a marvelous feeling I feel so alive again, my deppresion has gone, and I now feel as though I can tackle any thing I want to, and as a bounus I no longer suffer from the dreaded PMT evry month, I can not thank you enought for this new lease of life, I feel as though I have had a great weight lifted from

Female Age 22

writing to tell you how pleased I have been with the results of a steady loss of weight over the weeks

Female Age 63

Thunder and Lightning

"You won't make me live through a storm will you?"

"That won't serve any purpose." I told Mrs Wilson, "You're only going to be coming here for something like three or four hours of total treatment time. I can't afford to waste any of that by playing games with you, particularly when those games will serve no useful purpose. I think you've been watching some Hollywood Movies if you think that is the way to cure someone of a fear of thunder."

"I have seen it done on a film," she replied, "but I have a friend who is absolutely terrified of flies and she had treatment from a psychiatrist which involved her imagining herself to be in a room full of flies and later being told that she was actually going to be put in a room full of flies; so I know that's a method that they use to cure people of phobias."

"Did it cure your friend?"

"No. She couldn't face any more treatment, so sits at home with an aerosol of fly-spray on the arm of her chair and always carries a small one with her."

"So that isn't a method that is likely to cure, and I am certainly not going to use any such method with you. All we are going to do is go back and find out why you have this terror of storms. When we've found out what it is and when we have corrected the cause, then if you wish, and only if you wish, I will enable you to visualise a storm to prove to yourself that you have got rid of your fear."

I referred her back to a conversation I had with her and her husband in the reception area before she had come in for treatment. She had been too nervous to talk and her husband had told me that she wanted treatment for her fear of thunder. Apparently, this fear had been with her since late teenage and she was now in her sixties. For the last twenty years if any sort of storm threatened with any chance of producing thunder, she cowered under the stairs with the cupboard door closed and her husband used to have to take her in an occasional cup of tea. No matter how long the storm lasted she could not eat while thunder was threatened. Her husband told me that he just wanted her to have two or three treatments to calm her down and get her over this particular season of the year when thunder storms were most prevalent, then, if necessary, he would bring her back the following year for a similar treatment. I had told him that I was not prepared to do that sort of work, that if she came to me for treatment, she was coming to me for curative hypnotherapy. While I could not guarantee a cure, I was going to aim for one, because I did not want her the following year, telling her friends that hypnotherapy had not cured her when the thunder storms started again. They both accepted that, while it may take twice as long to affect a cure, I should try to achieve a permanent result.

It is interesting how somebody can develop a fear of thunder and yet no fear of lightning. She was well aware that the lightning had the ability to kill, whereas thunder was only a noise and never hurt anyone. If anyone ever had an incorrect reaction it was this lady. Her fear of thunder was a terrifying one, yet she had no fear of lightning whatsoever. In her case it only took as many treatments to cure her permanently, as they had expected to have for temporary alleviation of the sÿmptoms. Within three sessions, we had found out the reason for her fear and corrected her reaction.

At her very last session, when I asked her whether she was prepared to visualise walking through a terrible thunder storm, she readily agreed and came out of hypnosis with a big smile on her face. Her problem had started with a childish squabble when she was twelve. She and her sister were arguing over who should read a letter from her brother which was addressed to both of them. She had the letter in her hand and the argument became heated. Her sister picked up a knife off a table, threatened her with it and actually cut her forearm and at exactly the same time the man came to read the gas meter and knocked on the door. She associated the thunder of his knocking with the wound her sister had inflicted on her and developed her fear of thunder-like noises.

Only a few days had gone by before there was another thunder storm in the locality and she sent me the following letter:

Dear David,

I wish to thank you for the help that you have given to me over the past few weeks while I was attending your hypnotherapy centre,

Before I come to you for help I was a complete nervous wreck. I use to dread the summers coming because of the thunder storms. Now you have made me over come these fears. In the last storm that we had (the first since having tretment) I even had the courage to go out into the garden and watch it. which would never have happened before, it has taken a conciderable amount of my mind to over come these fears, People have comented on how calm I have become and how much better I am looking for it. I cannot thank you enough for the help that you have given me, my husband also wishes to send his thanks because he doesn't have to worry so much when he is at work.

Yours Sincerley,

Female Age 63

Thunder and lightning, as with all problems, varies in the number of treatments that are necessary because one has to go at the speed of the patient. Judith was one who took twice as long as the lady above. When she was telling me why she wanted treatment her hands were grasping each other in tension and there were beads of sweat on her top lip. She told me that she had always had the problem with thunder and lightning, that she had diarrhoea, and had to cover her head. I went through the usual procedure of explaining what hypnosis was like, how we would use the relaxed state to find out why she had this fear and then demonstrated to her what it felt like in hypnosis. She responded very well and went into a very plesant state of relaxation. However, on the second occasion when she came, although she relaxed well to start with, she became less relaxed as soon as I started to ask questions and started to bring in her conscious mind instead of allowing the answers to come to her without thought. She took me back to the war when her sister, brother and father were all killed in an air raid and her mother was seriously hurt and died the following year. She was obviously upset about recalling this event and there is certainly a sound of thunder and flashes that could be translated as lightning during an air-raid, but on questioning, it turned out that she had the problem long before this. She was twenty when the air-raid took place but she had had her problem since before she was ten years old.

I told her to visualise the incident that lay at the root of her problem. She saw something dark. She realised that it was the centre of a sun-flower and there were yellow petals around it and it was, she said, something to do with the explosions during the war. I could see how she could be conjuring up a picture of a sun-flower to represent the picture of an explosion but I also knew that we were dealing with facts not fantasy and I needed the precise, logical incident that had caused her problem. So we went back again to when she was eight years old, outside without any fear of thunder at all. She could see fields and bushes and it was daytime. She was happy. Then, suddenly, it went dark and she was outside a church and the sky was dark 'like thunder'. She was alone and afraid of the coming storm. She moved forwards from eight to nine years old, then forwards to ten when she was at school and the teacher said that there was a storm coming, told the children there was nothing to be frightened of and that they should all go to the window and watch it. She told them to count in between the flashes and the noise of the thunder so that they could tell the distance that the storm was from them.

This sounded to me as though it could be something to do with the cause of her fear. It may have been something the teacher said, which started the train of thought, but then she said that somebody had called her a coward and I asked her whether she had a fear of thunder and lightning at that time. She replied that she had. So the fear had its cause earlier in her life.

At the following session she told me about a fire at a factory at the end of her road, that there were quite often fires at this factory and on several occasions when she was a child, all the houses nearby had to be evacuated. Many incidents came out which could have some bearing on thunder or lightning; explosions, storms, war, fires, she was bringing all these in because she was partially using her conscious mind. Her subconscious was bringing out things that were on the same computer programme which had developed into the fear which had brought her for treatment, yet we still had not got the real cause because she was using her conscious mind to analyse and interpret before telling me what was in her mind. Yet the cause was so simple; when she was seven she was at a fireworks party and she and another couple of children, including her sister, were chased by some others and they hid in a dark scullery. Someone threw a lighted jumping-jack in the scullery and slammed the door, leaving them in the dark with this firework exploding and flashing. When this happened to her, her thoughts went back to something that had happened earlier that same evening when she had been given a sparkler to hold while it was burning and had actually burned her hand on it. She knew that fireworks could damage her, fireworks were dangerous, fireworks were able to hurt her and the firework in the scullery was making a noise like thunder and flashing like lightning. Just as one can make associations between fireworks and thunder and lightning, one can make other associations as this lady did. She had developed a fear of the rumble of heavy lorries going past her house because she associated that rumbling with thunder as well. Then shopping had become a nightmare to her because of the traffic on the road.

Most people who have a fear of thunder or of lightning have a fear of both, but just because this is usual, a hypnotherapist must not fall into the trap of assuming that this is the case. Hypnotherapy is treating the patients's interpretation of what has happened. That interpretation is made on the basis of previous experience and nobody had identical experiences. It is easy to assume that because one person describes their symptoms in the same way as another patient, the causes of their problem must be similar. It is easy to put people into pigeon-holes and to treat them with theories, but it is the individual's personal experiences which colour the way that they interpret events in their life; In other words, each person is completely unique, the way they interpret things is unique and therefore their problem is completely unique to them.

Each person has their own reason for their symptoms. That reason is always a logical one and is based on some mis-information. No two people have got the same mis-information in their minds which is why treatment has to be completely personal to that patient.

Dear David
I have just been through my first thunderstorm this year yes, I was nervous watching the build up of black clouds then the roll of thunder but for the first time ever I did not get into a panic. I am deeply grateful to you for your wonderful help.

Female Age 73

She actually watched the clouds build up this time and because she now knows she will not panic her tension for the next storm will be less. After a couple of storms with no panic and diminishing tension she will react normally.

Word Power

IMAGINE HEAT............

I mean it! Stop reading and imagine heat for just the next three or four seconds..

Out of all the many people who, hopefully, will be reading this book at some time or other, each one of you interpreted that word in your own particular way. You may have interpreted heat as relaxing in a hot bath, or being burnt by a cigarette end when a child, watching molten larva spewing out of a volcano, sleeping on a summer's beach or lying in a bed after a day on the beach burning up with sunburn. You may have thought of a hot bowl of soup or the surface of the sun or you could have thought of the heat of bodily contact, or of hard work in front of a foundry furnace or, if you are that way inclined, you may even have conjured up a vision of the fires of Hell.

One word that creates an infinite number of pictures, different pictures in every single mind. No two people can interpret the same words in exactly the same way. It is therefore essential that when guiding someone under hypnosis one is very careful about the choice of words and builds pictures step by step so that there can be no mistakes in the interpretation by the patient.

A couple of years ago I had a lady with a migraine problem who had told me that it was aggravated by bananas and cheese. We found out the cause of the migraine and corrected it. When she came for a final check-up, she confirmed that the cause of the migraine had been dealt with, re-interpreted completely and finally and that she would not have any further migraines. I then took the question a step further as I believe in checking everything three or four ways.

"As you've now got rid of the cause of your migraine and have confirmed that you will no longer have any attacks will bananas have any detrimental effect on you?"

I had the surprising answer; "Yes."

"Will cheese have any detrimental effect on you?"

Once again the answer was "Yes", and my heart went into my boots. It looked as though I was going to have to start again with this one, right at the very beginning.

Remember that when one is treating a patient one is up against a time limit as there are other patients waiting. You have to wipe these people out of your mind and concentrate exclusively on the one person you are treating. In my mind I had been certain that it was just a matter of checking up and then saying good-bye to this lady, but these two replies obviously made me really stop and think. My next question, however, made the whole thing clear in my mind.

"Are you telling me that eating bananas will cause you to have migraine?"

The answer came....."No".

"Will it aggravate migraine?"

Once again, the answer 'no'. I asked her the same questions about cheese but I had the same response, and then I realised that, of course, bananas and cheese will have an effect on her and a detrimental effect because if she eats too much of them, as with anything else, she will get fat. I checked and this, indeed, was how she had interpreted my question. Nothing whatsoever to do with migraine. She was only coming for treatment for migraine but nevertheless she took my words literally that eating either of these two substances could have a detrimental effect, they could make her fat. As you read the various cases in this book you will realise how many of the problems caused by people have their roots in the words that somebody used. Case after case of words that were either wrongly used by someone or more usually, wrongly interpreted by the patient who comes to me for treatment. Words do indeed have a terrible power. One lady developed a lack of confidence and both asthma and dermatitis due to her mother saying that she was too stupid to use a new toy typewriter and taking it away from her when the girl was only four years old and could hardly be expected to spell correctly never mind put sentences down on paper. Another lady put on weight because of rejection when she overheard her husband saying that after twenty years it would be nice to have a change of woman, when in reality he was only joking and neither before nor during the twelve years after those words had he given her any indication whatsoever that he wanted a change of woman or genuinely rejected her. He had made a joke but she did not interpret it in that way in her subconscious.

Many people on finishing the treatment start to worry about the words they use and the way they treat their children but there is no way that one can guard against starting incorrect programmes in someone's computer. Maybe the best way to avoid starting any wrong reactions would be not to talk to them, but one then has the problem of interpretation of that by a child. If one of their parents will not talk to them, the child may interpret that in the wrong way. So even this approach could cause problems. Whenever I think of words and the problems that they can cause my mind goes back to one young lady of about twenty-four who was suffering terrible tension and an overwhelming complusion to work. She had a full time job five days a week, eight hours a day and she then worked behind a bar every evening and had a third job on Saturdays and Sundays. All she did was take time off to eat and sleep. She had no friends although she had a very pleasant personality and would certainly have been quite popular as a barmaid. She just never gave herself time to make friends yet she did not do these jobs for money.

She had recently had to stop work because she had driven herself into a nervous breakdown which she had now overcome but could see herself back in the old routine once more. She knew she was going to suffer the same illness again.

We went back with her to nursery school where the head mistress used to stand in front of her school each day beating a drum and making the children sing, "Work, work, work and don't be lazy". My patient had realised that when she went into hospital to have her tonsils out she would not be able to work. Her interpretation was that she would be lazy and it had been drummed into her that laziness was just about the greatet sin imaginable. So from that moment, before the age of five, she developed into a workaholic. She did not want to be lazy but she was being forced into it and the only way she could fight against it was by working, working and working more and more which was the pattern of her life from then on. She branded herself as lazy because of the teacher's words and she was doing everything possible to reverse her own self-image.

Mothers and teachers, of course, are the people most dangerous because they are most in contact with children who are having fresh experiences and thus developing new reactions. One is born with the basic programming of survival, protection and comfort; everything else is acquired as situations and emotions are experienced. Even a few words said in front of a child too young to understand them can cause a problem later in life. Apparently the sound of the words is registered in the mind and later on, when the understanding comes, they can then interpret that old remark which was incomprehensible at the time it was made. A sufferer from premature ejaculation took me back to when he was very young and his mother was drying him after a bath. His father came into the bathroom and his mother compared her two sons, "Roger won't be as big as John, you can tell that by the size of his penis, he'll always be small". That remark caused sexual inadequacy in adulthood.

It is almost impossible to believe that premature ejaculation can be caused by words, and more particularly when those words were used at the age of three. Yet those words were the cause of not only his premature ejaculation, but his first marriage breaking up and his second becoming very shakey. From that one comment he built up a resentment against his whole family, against his mother for making the comment, his father for accepting it and his brother for being the person that he was measured against and found wanting. He also developed a complex about his height quite apart from his sexual problem.

We have to use our imagination to see the meaning behind words and this is what makes words so powerful. Imagination is more important than reality - we always react to what we believe has happened not necessarily to what actually happened. If our imagination makes mistakes we have a mistaken reaction.

Up to the age of twenty-four one of my patients had no trouble at all with menstruation but reacted with migraine when her Doctor told her that a lot of women have problems with their periods: "as the body retains water, so you get a headache".

Migraine and tinnitus (the continuous sound of ringing or the sound of sea in the ears) are often developed as a barrier against unwelcome words. One lady used to hide money from her husband so that he could not waste it. During one argument with him she said that he would not be getting much more because when the last of her children left home she was going as well. He retaliated by saying that she would not have the guts, and in spite of the fact that she did leave her husband, she still had the fear that there were situations in her life which she would not have the guts to face. When difficult situations arose she developed tinnitus to block out her husband's words.

One man had a problem of shyness, lack of confidence and unnatural blushing, which was caused when he was 7 years old at school and the teacher called him an idiot because he did not know the answer to a question. When talking to other children in the class after the lesson, it turned out that none of them knew the answer to that question. In reality the teacher was the idiot. She had not explained properly to the class. The fault was hers, but the words that she used were directed to only one person in the class and he was shown up as an idiot by the one in authority. From there on his reaction was one of lack of confidence - not only because he was an idiot but because he had been made to look an idiot in front of all his friends and this was re-inforced three years later when his father criticised his bad use of grammar saying: "I don't know why I bother to send you to school."

Many people come with problems such as headaches, migraine or tinnitus yet few people realise how words cause other physical problems such as arthritis or back pain. The lady wearing a surgical collar because of her arthritic neck had developed her problem due to working with a woman who was much better educated and far better off financially. My patient believed she was superior but as this woman was continually pushing her superiority in front of everybody else, the lady I was treating strongly disliked her and objected to 'looking up to her'. As the other woman was physically taller as well as being educationally and financially on a higher plane, my lady developed her arthritis to get round the necessity of 'looking up to her'. If she did not look up to her then she was not superior, she was on the same level as the lady having treatment. That lady has now disposed of her surgical collar, having no further need for it.

Such innocent words as 'just like your mother' caused one person to develop stomach pains similar to those her mother had and another lady with terrible chest pains was convinced that she had a heart problem, though no medical tests could discover anything at all. She had developed those pains thirty years ago when she was fifteen as a punishment for the slight sexual feelings she had when her father hit her left breast. She knew that she should not have feelings like that towards her father. The girl of three who wandered into her father's bedroom while he was getting dressed and said: "dad, you've got a tail", developed continual headaches and digestive problems from the tension caused by her father's angry rection: "Get that child out of here, I don't want her in here. I don't want her." With words like that, she had a very good excuse to experience rejection.

Words cause so many problems because they require imagination to interpret them and because they are the means by which human beings communicate. They communicae their feelings, their emotions, their fears more by words than by any other means. A person translates their feelings into words and in the translation errors can creep in, the words are accepted by somebody else and then translated, once again, into that person's feelings and emotions and once again there is a chance of additional error and we are back with the situation of reacting, not to reality, but to what we imagine to be reality - the two things may be completely different.

As a migraine sufferer for eighteen years I was litterally becoming disabled through frequent attacks lasting two or three ~~times~~ ~~a~~ days at a time. These being so severe that I have banged my head against a wall in trying to get some kind of relief.

In the past twelve monthes I have spent some weeks in hospital because the migraine attacks were leaving me partially paralysed, similar to a mild stroke. The doctors were unable to find a cure for me and so were giving me narcotic drugs as pain relievers.

My own G.P. suggested hypnotherapy to me and he certainly could not have recconended a better cure. I feel so much better and I can now lead a normal life and not be ruled by whether I shall have a migraine attack or not.

Not only was treatment beneficial to me, but to my whole family. life is normal again

Once againr i thankyou for all you have done

Yours gratefully

Female Age 45

Sexual Guilt

"I can't come."

"Have you ever been able to?" I asked her.

"Never." She said. "I've got near it on a few occasions but usually as soon as the feelings start, they go within seconds."

"Do you mean when your sexual feelings start or when the feeling that you're going to come start?"

"The sexual feelings come and long before I get near anything really worthwhile they just dissipate."

She was obviously a lot more at ease now that she had told me the worst she could possibly think of, but she still was not entirely happy about talking about her problem so I decided to relax her and start the treatment without any more explanations apart from saying that we knew that there was nothing physically wrong with her otherwise she would not have those sexual feelings. There had to be something in her mind that was stopping her getting full enjoyment out of sex. I pointed out that normal sexual feelings started in the mind, which controls all feelings and emotions and all we had to do was find out why she was not allowing herself to have full sexual satisfaction and put that right. When she lay back in her chair, I started to talk her into relaxation but suddenly she sat up in the chair and started to cry. I calmed her down and then started once more; this time when she sat up she said, "I can't relax, I can't relax."

"Are you saying that you can't relax or that you mustn't let yourself relax?" I asked her.

"I mustn't relax," she said.

"OK, don't worry about it Sonia, just lean back in the chair and listen to me." I did what I found to be one of the most difficult things I had ever done. To take someone into deep relaxation without using the word 'relax'. The word 'relaxation' has become such a part of me over the years of practising hypnotherapy that it came automatically to my tongue. However, by talking to her without using the word we eventually reached the state of hypnosis but I had scribbled on her record card, in big letters 'Will Not Let Herself Relax' because even at this early stage it seemed obvious that she had a real problem here from her reaction to the word.

Sonia was one of the most dramatic women that I had ever come across. At her first visit she was fully prepared clutching a very large white man's handkerchief, expecting to cry, and later on in the treatment, when I asked her to imagine something, she acted it out. Usually people will lie there in the chair and just let my words form pictures in their mind but Sonia sat up, she moved her hands, she did everything physically as well as mentally. She acted out every single suggestion that I put to her and everything that she conjured up in her own mind.

For example, when she saw herself standing outside a door, I asked her to open the door. She reached out her hand as if to put it on a door handle and then pulled her arms back as if she was opening a door. When she told me there was nothing at all on the other side of the door, I finally got her to admit that she had only pretended to open it. Thus, with her ability to refuse to relax, her ability to try and trick me, she was, all the way through the treatment, using her control and allowing me only to guide her as far as she was prepared to go.

After the initial relaxation I answered one or two more of her questions and made one or two things plain to her, asking her for some background information which I thought was necessary. She was 49 years old, married, with a daughter of fifteen and her real problem was not her inability to achieve orgasm. This was of immense importance to her but she felt that there was something very wrong because she had no emotions for either her husband or her child. She also suffered from headaches, which were more or less continuous, and also from insomnia.

Four years previously she had hypnosis from her doctor who in her words "Got her back into her husbands' bed," although this was only temporary. Apparently the doctor had done this purely and simply by putting her into hypnosis, getting her to visualise a sexual scene and recreating sexual feelings in her body without any attempt to find out why she was blocking them. Without dealing with the cause, the effect had to be only temporary and she was now at my clinic in the hope of a permanent cure.

She was a really difficult person to deal with because of her dramatics, but gradually, the story emerged that her father had died when she was two and a half leaving her mother with just Sonia and an elder brother. Their mother was a dominating woman who showed her no affection and knocked her around on the pretext that someone had to and there was no father to do it.

The three of them lived in a two bedroomed house with my patient sharing a double bed with her mother. When Sonia was ten years old the mother's boyfriend used to come into the bedroom early in the mornings and 'make love' to Sonia's mother while Sonia was lying next to her in the same bed. Apparently this happened on eight or ten occasions, but on one occasion, he came in one morning to find that Sonia's mother had got up early and left the house. As usual he had undressed in the bathroom and came into the bedroom naked and ready for sex. Twelve year old Sonia was the only person there and he started to play with her sexually which gave her great feelings of pleasure but also of guilt because she knew the man belonged to her mother. At the same time, having watched the two of them in bed she knew there was a lot of pleasure to be gained and she wanted to experience it - after all, her mother gave her none.

Every now and then the guilt overrode the pleasure and she tried to stop but he kept telling her to "Relax and enjoy it" and in the end she did. She enjoyed it to such an extent that she knew that her mother would punish her terribly, not only for allowing herself to enjoy it but also because it was with her mother's boyfriend. She felt guilty about stealing from her mother the sensations that she was experiencing. Being told to relax was followed by a terrible feeling of guilt and fear of punishment. Therefore, she naturally could not respond to me telling her to relax and the guilt from the pleasure she experienced now prevented her enjoying sex. We steadily worked through her problems stemming from this incident and gradually disposed of her headaches which she had developed as a defence against having sex with her husband. Her guilt meant that she should not get enjoyment out of sex and the only way to make sure she was not going to enjoy it was not to have it. Every now and then, however, she and her husband had sex, but as soon as she felt feelings begin to rise her guilt overrode them.

Many people believe that the inability to enjoy sex has to be caused by an unpleasant sexual incident, that is, an incident that was sexually unpleasant, but, as in Sonia's case, the usual cause of a sex problem is a pleasant experience followed by guilt or a feeling of being 'dirty'. Sexually, they enjoy it and it is usually the situation that causes the problem, the person with whom they had sex, or the circumstances surrounding the event. In fact, most people who have problems which are based on a sexual incident actually enjoyed that incident and it was the enjoyment that caused the problem. Often this can go back to a very, very early age like the lady of thirty-five who started her sexual adventures when she was nine, with a neighbour.

She and her sister were in her neighbour's house and she wanted to explore sex. She got the neighbour to ask her sister to go up the road to the shop so that she could encourage the neighbour, who she knew was interested in her sexually. She used the words 'He sexually assaulted me' which just shows our conditioning as she had already told me before that she had deliberately planned to be on her own with him and therefore this could hardly be called an assault. She admitted that she led him on, that she was the leader, but still used the word 'assault'. He only used his hands on her but her pleasure was so intense, and his was obviously just as intense when she was handling his penis and later, having had a couple of other experiences in between, at eleven years old she more or less blackmailed an 'old man' who owned a junk shop into doing the same thing for her and she had a terrible feeling of rejection when he would not let her touch him sexually.

Quite often, these feelings that cause problems do not arise at the time of the incident, it is only later when other people's judgments are imposed on one, that one refers back and develops guilt. Such a one was Ruth.

Ruth had a weight problem stemming from the time when she walked into her mother's bedroom and found her having intercourse with her son (Ruth's brother) who was seventeen. Later her mother took her aside and told her of the delights of sexual feelings and that night joined Ruth in her bed and introduced her to the pleasures of sex. This went on for three years on a more or less regular basis until Ruth realised that she was the only person she knew who was having enjoyment sexually from her mother. She knew about lesbian sex but never associated it with having that sort of enjoyment from one's mother. She developed a guilt which stopped her having sex with her husband and her husband started to have affairs outside the marriage. When she realised her husband no longer wanted sex with her she experienced rejection and, as we have seen before, rejection is one of the most common reasons for women to put on weight.

The number of people with sexual problems due to an unpleasant sexual experience is very small indeed in comparison to the number of people who have had a problem of some sort caused by a pleasurable sexual experience. The range of symptoms caused by guilt about enjoying sex is almost too numerous to mention. They can vary from depression to insomnia, from obesity to alcoholism and from anxiety to alopecia totalis. This last symptom came into my consulting room in the form of a very attractive lady of nearly forty who, the previous year had, over a period of five months, lost all her hair. Her eyelashes and eybrows had disappeared at more or less the same time as the hair on her head, her pubic hair, the hair under her arms and every single hair on her arms and her legs had also disappeared completely. This was obviously a terrible punishment for a woman as attractive as she was. She had a good figure, was elegantly dressed and had a very pleasant face indeed though her manner at the consultation caused me some concern as she appeared to be rather superior. I knew almost from the first sentences that were exchanged that she was going to be a time-consuming person who would want to have every question justified to her before she would give an answer. At the first session of actual treatment, all I could find out was that her alopecia was punishment, punishment because she was guilty. I could not make any further progress than this. At the next session, however, she came out with the words "....immorality. I'm cheap, I always have been. Lots of sexual incidents before marriage. Mum told me I was cheap. Sex is dirty sometimes. Only sometimes. John used me. I am a slut. I always have been."

She then visualised sitting in a graveyard with a boy. They were having a smoke, some sort of drug - there was no need for me to find out what sort it was. They then went to the cinema and "He just left me half-way through the picture, when he had done what he wanted he left me, he just touched me, I was spaced out. I'm a slag, I'm fat and ugly, I'm awful. That's all they want." She had been fifteen years old at the time and she had welcomed his touch. She had already experienced intercourse to orgasm - that is what she had wanted on that occasion. Just before I brought her out of hypnosis she said, "I loved John, but he had what he wanted and left me." I asked her when she had been with John and it turned out that it was the previous year she had sex with him. So it was not just sex before marriage because she had been married for fourteen years.

She had told me that she was ashamed of her own vanity, that she knew that she was extremely good-looking and she was extremely vain. She said it was her vanity that made her betray her husband and that John had hurt her but it was only when I asked her three or four times that she admitted that he had not physically hurt her, only her vanity had been hurt. Time after time we went back until it emerged that when she was a school, at around six years old, one of the other girls had 'touched her'. The girl's father had seen what had happened and my patient got the blame. "It wasn't me, I didn't do it. She said I did and now Debbie wants me. Why can't they leave me alone? It's wrong, help me, please help me, why won't people leave me alone?"

I felt now that we were nearing the core of her problem, particularly when a few moments later she admitted that a couple of years after this incident another girl at school had experimented sexually with her. With the first girl she had no pleasure at all but she had some pleasure with the second one although it was still really just a game. But Debbie was a different matter - she welcomed her touch. This lesbian affair had started only two years ago and she welcomed Debbie's touch. She has been brought to orgasm by Debbie on several occasions. She knew it was wrong, she knew she was guilty and when Debbie commented on her beautiful hair, she felt that it was her hair that had attracted this girl to her and therefore she took the logical step of losing her hair - every single bit of it!

As with any problem, there can be a tremendous time lapse between the incident that caused the problem and the incident which actually triggered the symptoms. A good example of this was a lady of seventy-five. She had originally come with depression and an eye twitch, tembling of the arms and legs, a sleep problem, a problem of breathing due to tension and with thoughts of suicide. She had had hypnosis from her doctor which, in spite of being tremendously expensive, had not done her any good at all. She had been in the hands of psychiatrists for four years. She was now going to a psychiatric hospital as an outpatient to attend what they called 'relaxation classes'. This consisted of relaxing muscles in her body, starting at the feet, but by the time she had got to her knees, she had already lost track of what she was trying to do and was back with her worries once more. Her psychiatrist had also arranged for her to do basket weaving and jig-saws on the days she attended relaxation classes. She strongly disliked both of these activities, but even worse, because she also had agoraphobia, the psychiatrist made her go shopping.

Obviously, with treatment such as this, she was getting steadily worse and had been thinking of 'ending everything' more and more often. We went back with her to her late teenage when she had had an abortion. The depression was due to a belief that she had committed murder and was not a fit person to go on living. We dealt with the depression but she was still suffering from tension. In particular, her breathing was causing problems. We went back to her early twenties when she was going out with a boy and having sex with him. He went into the army and his brother started to take her out. "He was supposed to be looking after me but worked his way into my life."

The second brother told her that the boy she had been having sex with had 'a disease'. She translated this as a venereal disease but had no symptoms herself so did not worry. Twelve years or so later, her old boyfriend had gangrene in his leg which was amputated and this 'confirmed' to her that it was V.D. Forty years later when she had an attack of cystitis she believed that the disease had finally caught up with her, in spite of the fact that she had had no intercourse for almost twenty years. This caused her tension, not just the fact that she believed that she had this disease but that her husband had probably caught it from her and any day might wake up and find that he was suffering from it also and know that it was his wife that had transmitted it to him. She was certain that he had never had sex apart from with her, so her husband would know and any moment might face her with her secret.

This lady was unfortunate in the psychiatrist who was giving her treatment. The psychiatrist had told her not to be silly, that her fears and tension were caused by a delusion. She repeated that she was suffering from delusions and this, of course, aggravated her tension. It caused her sleeping problems as she thought she was losing her mind and becoming insane. She was scared of the psychiatrist, "All she does is pat me on the shoulder and tell me to relax. How can I relax? If I could relax would she be giving me antidepressant tablets? And I can't give those up now, can I? But all she says is 'just relax'. I dare not tell her that I'm coming to you for treatment."

When I had cured this lady, she had sufficient courage to tell her psychiatrist that she did not want any more of her tablets and eventually had to admit that she had been treated by hypnotherapy and felt cured. Her psychiatrist was shocked and annoyed but by this time my patient had developed so much confidence in herself that she rode the storm. The meeting ended with the psychiatrist agreeing that there was no doubt that she had been cured and congratulated her for having hypnotherapy.

Dear David Lesser,

Just to say I've been off the pills for 2 weeks and, so far, I'm doing extremely well. I have my ups and downs all the time but I've got an inner resilience that I've never had before.

Part of me has got better and is going to stay better and it does seem to be an ongoing process of improvement.

You made it all very simple and easy to understand and you did me a big favour in re-educating my attitude to the subconscious — Thank you very much for that.

All the best with your work.

Female Age 28

The Punishment Fits The Crime

Our built-in computers are far more logical than the judicial system in western countries. They are far more like some of the punishments meted out in Islamic countries where a thief may have his hand cut off so that it can never again steal.

Many people have an illness which is a direct punishment -but more than a punishment because it can prevent them saying the same thing or doing the same action again in the future. The boy who at four years old threw a stone at a playmate and cut his head open, developed asthma to prevent him from exerting himself. Not only was exertion by stone throwing prevented but he was unable to swim, play football or exert himself in any way at all from the age of five to the age of nineteen when he came to me for treatment. The lady previously mentioned who had suffered a complete loss of all the hair on her body was not only punished by that loss because she was a very vain woman (her own words), but because her lesbian lover was attracted by her beautiful hair. She lost the one thing that appeared to attract women to her because sex between women was not acceptable to her morals.

The girl who was told by her father to take the dog to the vet and went out instead chasing 'a worthless boy', developed extremely unsightly and painful acne when the dog died, not just as a punishment, but also to prevent her going out again. Her face was such a mess that she wanted no-one to look at her. She certainly did not want to attract any men. Even in the hottest weather she walked with a scarf wrapped round the lower half of her face and sat in my reception room with a book in her lap and her chin right down on her chest so that nobody could see her face. The lady who had stolen a pair of tights from a shop (and I believe this to be the only dishonest act she ever did) developed arthritis in her hands and wrists. While many people will develop a stammer to give themselves time to ensure that they are saying the right thing due to an incident that has caused a lack of confidence, others will develop it as a hesitation to give them a chance to alter their words because in the past they said something for which they feel thay should be punished.

One lady of twenty-seven who had been married for nine years had been trying to have a baby for more or less the whole of that time. She told me that her fallopian tubes were continually blocked.

Surgery had been performed several times but the tubes were immediately becoming blocked again. Apparently the surgeons had finally removed one of her ovaries and one tube when they unblocked the other tube. The remaining tube had blocked once more. The logical cause of her problem was partially punishment but mainly because her sub-conscious mind did not trust her to get pregnant. At the age of fifteen she had become pregnant and her parents, against her wishes, had insisted that she have an abortion which was duly performed. She had not wanted the abortion. She considered it murder and was preventing herself from repeating the crime. If she did not get pregnant she could not commit murder - a perfect example of the punishment fitting the crime. Last Christmas, I had a card from her enclosing a photograph of her children, a boy who is now three, and a girl of about ten months. She had accepted the logic of the situation which had altered over the intervening dozen years. Now she was not subject to anyone's influence; now she was the mistress of her own body and could go through with pregnancy to a successful conclusion. She conceived her first child less than three months after we completed treatments - after eight years of fruitless attempts.

Punishment by the sub-conscious is often far greater than the 'crime' warrants. Most punishments are, in fact, for non existent crimes. Once again we are back to imagination - people imagine that they have done something wrong and react accordingly. The girl who had the abortion was under her parents' control, the woman who had the lesbian affair had not done anyone any damage apart from the damage she had done to herself with her feelings of guilt. She had not even damaged her husband's opinion of himself because she still preferred heterosexual activities to homosexual ones. The boy who had thrown the stone was so shocked when his friend fell to the ground with his head bleeding that there was no way that he would ever do a similar thing again in the future. He needed no constant reminder to stop, he needed no physical disability to make sure that he could not exert himself. There was no way that boy would ever have done a similar thing in the future yet he had suffered really chronic asthma for fourteen years, which is about the length of time a person spends in jail for a coldblooded, premeditated murder.

Although a small percentage of patients have developed their symptoms as a punishment, one virtually never has a patient for treatment who has done something that merits the punishment.

Anyone who has actually committed a murder has either done it in anger and will control their anger automatically because of the terrible consequences, or has planned it, decided to do it and carried out the deed. A person who actually takes the time to plan and actually commit a murder is not the sort of person who is going to feel guilt, therefore they do not develop a problem.

One of the biggest fears of patients is that I am going to find out something terrible that they did in their past, yet apart from the fact that I cannot MAKE them reveal anything to me, people who develop problems are not people who have done anything really bad. It is their interpretation of small things; building their own mountains out of molehills. Because they are the sort of people who CAN feel guilt, they will react with guilt and thus with punishment to trivial things in their lives. They will do something mistakenly, something without thought or something in anger, and will then feel guilty. In many cases the sub-conscious will produce a symptom which is not only a punishment but the sort of punishment that prevents them from doing a similar thing in the future. This is a protection for them - it protects them from causing themselves an even heavier load of guilt in the future.

Having their 'guilty secrets' exposed is the thing that creates a lot of apprehension in patients, yet such guilt is only imaginary. Hundreds of people come through my consulting rooms with guilt as the basis of their problem even if they do not consciously experience the feeling of guilt. Their symptoms may be extremely distressing yet the cause of their original guilt is always something that, consciously, they consider insignificant.

One lady had been forced to give up work for three months because she could do nothing but weep. At the consultation I was unable to get much information from her through her tears, nor was I able to get her to really absorb what I was saying to her. Later we went back with her to when she was about seven years old, visiting her Grandmother who lived only a few streets away. She was a regular visitor, almost every weekend, and many times Grandma had shown her a very beautiful locket on a necklace, telling her that the locket really belonged to my patient. When she was older she would be allowed to have it permanently. In the meantime Grandma would only show it to her, let her handle it, but never let her put it on.

Naturally enough, this little girl had a desire to wear the locket.

After all, she had been told it was hers, she wanted to wear it, she wanted to show it off to her friends. She could not understand how it was hers yet she was not allowed to keep it. One day, Grandma fell asleep and the girl took the locket, put it round her neck and went out to show her friends. There was no damage to the locket, neither did she lose it. She returned it safely to the same place before Grandma woke up again but she knew that she was guilty, she knew that if her Grandma ever found out she would consider her untrustworthy; in other words, she KNEW that she was untrustworthy. Ever since then, throughout her life, being a guilty sort of person, she took all the guilt on herself for anything that ever went wrong. She continually reinforced this feeling that all fault was hers, until she ended up having hypnotherapy as the doctor's anti-depressants were ineffective. Such are the silly incidents that lie at the root of almost everyone's problems, from the young boy trying to teach chickens of a few days old how to swim underwater and consequently drowning them, to the woman who, realising that her adopted mother was not as attractive or as young as the mothers of her school friends decided, one day, not to walk down the road hand-in-hand, but to walk a few paces behind her, then afterwards felt guilt about what she had done.

Guilt is not only a punishment, it can also prevent similar actions in the future, just as the lady with arthritis was attempting to stop herself from shoplifting, and the girl with acne was stopping herself going out - punishment often fits the IMAGINARY crime.

Your treatment has been the key to a more relaxed, happier and confident me. Obviously, the day-to-day problems are still there, I just have a different approach to them now.

I thank you from the bottom of my heart for what you have done, it certainly seems to have "done the trick" with me.

Female Age 41

For four long years, I've walked in shame
And loathed my own face since they came
My doctor prescribed pills and lotions
And I've bought creams and special potions
I changed my diet, no chips, no fudge
But painful acne wouldn't budge
Out of the window my confidence flew
I was sad and depression grew
Then I read a notice in the paper
And thought to myself "Whats this caper.
I phoned and David said "come to me.
You need my help we both agree"
Over six sessions we found at last
An unusual incident in my past
Had caused my guilt to overspill
And my face with spots did fill
David said "You weren't to blame
So spots go back from whence you came'
And such improvement now I see
David, Thanks for helping me!!

Female Age 24

Is Belief Necessary?

"So I really was hypnotised then?" Penny said in surprise as she stood firmly cemented to the middle of the floor.

To put it mildly, I was even more amazed than her. After curing her of half-a-dozen problems she still did not think that she had been in hypnosis and it had taken a silly trick to convince her.

Penny had volunteered to be treated in front of a group to whom I was teaching hypnotherapy, and this last visit was just to check that all the causes to her problems had been rectified and all her symptoms had disappeared or were steadily diminishing and would disappear. She had received a total of ten treatments which was more than the average that patients receive but Penny had far more than just one problem.

The first time she came she was in her own words 'A mess'. She was suffering from tinnitus: A complaint that is enough to drive people to desperate lengths. She had a bell continuously ringing loudly in one ear, so loudly that she had put her head close to her mothers on one occasion, and asked her whether she could also hear the noise. In her other ear she had a continual sound of the sea. These noises were unremitting, going on through the whole of each day and all through the nights as well.

In addition, Penny had migraine attacks several times each week. She also had an unreasoning fear of cancer and mild, but growing, agoraphobia. She had a chronic sinus problem, and a continuous feeling that she was going to fall down and always had a lot of headaches. She had a terrible lack of confidence in herself, and yet, having cured all these problems in only a couple of months, she still did not believe that she had ever been in hypnosis.

On this final occasion of her check-up, the trainees on the course were asking questions and the subject of acceptance of suggestions by the therapist came up. I asked Penny if she would be prepared to co-operate in a little experiment. Having assured her that she would be able to go into hypnosis standing up, without falling, Penny stood in the middle of the floor while I put her into hypnosis and I then told her that I was pouring a bucket of quick-setting cement over her feet and that she could actually feel the cement setting hard, encasing both her feet in one solid lump of concrete. I then took her out of hypnosis, she looked down at her feet, and seeing no sign of cement, looked up at me and said:

"I feel a fool standing here in front of you lot." I said to her that she could come over to where I was and sit down, but Penny was firmly stuck to the floor. She could move neither of her feet. That was what convinced her that she had been in hypnosis. Normally, of course, I never do these sort of tricks. My sole aim is to cure people of their problems, but we were talking about accepting suggestions which is the secret of hypnosis: Acceptance by the patient without analysis, without criticism, just as she had done. Not only to cement her feet to the floor, but to cure her of her problems.

Being the 'nervous type' Penny had a problem at first in accepting the audience although this was only a small group of people who were all genuinely interested in learning, with the intention of becoming professional hypnotherapists. Her speed of response was quite amazing because each one of the problems had to be dealt with separately. Each one had its own individual cause. Her tinnitus was caused at the age of 41 when her doctor telephoned her and bluntly told her over the phone, without any warning, that her husband was seriously ill, that he had six months to live. These were the sort of words that she did not want to hear, hence the development of hearing impairment in the ear to which she had held the phone when she was told the news. The tinnitus in her other ear was caused before her wedding. Her father had been decorating the living room for the wedding and she and her father had an argument while they were having a cup of tea. She lost her temper and threw her cup at the wall and started to leave the room. Her father, who had been working hard on her behalf, then lost his temper and, in the middle of lighting his cigarette, threw his lighter at her and hit her under the left ear. Her ear problem was an extension of the punishment by that lighter. She knew she had done wrong by throwing that cup and spoiling her father's hard work which had been done on her behalf.

Her headaches went back to an earlier event. When she was a young girl her mother was very proud of her long hair. "She won't stop brushing it, she brushes it and brushes it until it gives me a headache, I hate that hair, I don't want long hair, I hate it." Later on, at the age of thirteen, there was an incident where her mother was brushing her hair and she was developing a headache once more because of the continual strain on her hair. Her mother kept brushing and Penny finally could not keep still as it seemed to be going on for ever. She fidgetted and her mother hit her on the back of her head with the hairbrush.

That must have been the last straw for Penny because shortly after that she had all her long hair cut off without telling her mother who was terribly upset when she came home and saw her daughter with short hair. When she thought back to the hours and hours her mother had spent making her hair look nice, she felt guilty about having it all cut off. Guilt deserves punishment and the easy way, the obvious way for Penny to punish herself, was by recreating the headaches that her mother used to create.

The interesting thing about Penny was disbelief that she had ever been hypnotised. It is quite a common feeling amongst patients, even after they have been cured, but I also get numerous patients who come and say "I don't believe in hypnotherapy but my doctor has suggested that I come." "You helped a neighbour of mine but I think she just accepted what you said." - Which is, of course, the truth. Belief in hypnotherapy is no requirement for a cure. Even a straight forward disbelief is no hindrance as long as the patient is prepared to go along with the words that I use. Obviously, some people do have considerable resistance because of a fear of being taken over, because of a belief that it is something to do with witchcraft or even, as one minister of religion told a lady who was coming here for treatment, it is 'dabbling in Satanic practices'.

A similar remark such as this was once made to a nurse by a surgeon at a hospital in which she was working. Many people make silly remarks about hypnotherapy through sheer ignorance. No-one who has ever experienced hypnosis or had a course of hypnotherapy ever finds it frightening, unpleasant or anything except a completely logical treatment using the patient's logic to cure themselves. Anyone who tries to persuade someone out of hypnotherapy is talking from ignorance, and although some people come not believing they can be helped, not believing that they can be hypnotised or with a fear of hypnosis, they come because no-one else has been able to help them.

There are groups of people who have formed tinnitus associations or associations of people with depression or alcoholism. There are many types of these associations around. Penny was one who had joined a tinnitus association but she had had the commonsense to realise that all these people are doing is trying to learn to live with their problem not trying to get cured. This was why she had originally come for hypnotherapy with the tinnitus as her major complaint. She had realised that the problem with associations such as these are that they give the sufferers the belief that they can not be cured and therefore, they very rarely come for proper treatment having once joined fellow sufferers. It is rather on the line of group therapy practised for people in depression. Getting a number of people suffering from depression gathered together so often means that each one of them reinforces the depression in the others and will pick up additional symptoms.

When Penny first came for treatment she did not believe that she could be helped. She thought that the only way out of her continual headaches and the permanent noises in her head which were nearly driving her mad, was to kill herself. She had tried almost everything starting with pills from the doctor, psychiatric treatment, acupuncture, faith-healing and as in so many cases I was, in her words, her 'last resort'. Obviously, if she had been through all these other types of treatments, which appeared to her to be the most likely ones to succeed, and I was bottom of her list, she had very little faith. Most patients who cross my threshold feel the same.

Faith, however, is not necessary. She was prepared to accept. All the way through the treatment, she never once believed that she had been in hypnosis until I did that little trick to which she agreed for the benefit of the trainees on my course. Belief, therefore, is not a necessity for a cure. The only necessity is co-operation, and I was very pleased when I found, leaning against the front door of my premises one morning, an envelope containing one of the regular bulletins issued by the tinnitus association with a note from Penny suggesting that I might like to contact these people. She had travelled seven miles by foot and by bus just to put this booklet against my front door, without even ringing the bell to have a word with me. Naturally I read the booklet which dealt with all sorts of things apart from curing the problem of tinnitus - it dealt with fitting devices to mask the noise, to make louder noises than people already have in their heads and other means of trying to suppress the symptoms. Page after page, without any suggestion, without any words at all about the possible cure for the sufferers of this very, very distressing problem. I also had a letter from Penny, part of which read as follows:

Since having Hypnotherapy Treatment from you, I have noticed a marked improvement in the reduction of the Bell Noises in my head "Tinnitus". When I came to you the noise was unbearable, now it is at a "tolerable" level. I feel I can live with this level of head noise, but before it was like signals coming out of my ears

also thank you for taking that dreadful Migraine away, and the headaches, which are nearly non-existant now, instead of daily.

Female Age 48

A few months later Penny 'phoned to say her tinnitus had disappeared completely and she could hardly remember what her headaches or migraine used to feel like.

Deafness can be caused in a similar way and the following letter was sent by a man of 87 years who had been completely deaf in one ear for 6 years and whose hearing in the other was so reduced that at the first few sessions I had great difficulty in getting him in the necessary state of relaxation.

Dear Mr. Lesser. Thank you for your hypnotherapy treatment for my deafness which has resulted in more acute hearing.

Male Age 87

Failures

There are hypnotherapists who claim that they never have a failure. They say that people who do not succeed in losing their problems are, themselves, failures. That the failure does not lie with the hypnotherapist but with the patient.

There is some truth in this as the hypnotherapist acts purely and simply as the necessary guide to the patient and it is the patient, by accepting what is done, who cures himself and therefore failure must be due to the patient. However, I feel that at least a part of the blame must be put on to the hypnotherapist who has been unable to explain fully how the treatment will proceed in words that are acceptable to the patient. Many times a patient will come in after one or two treatments saying that they do not feel any benefit, although I do not expect them to feel any better until the cause has been uncovered and corrected. Some of them may feel a benefit before then, occasionally others may experience exactly the opposite effect. They may suffer an increase in their symptoms instead of a decrease. As has been demonstrated previously in this book, everyone has a logical reason for their problem; in other words, they believe that their problem is necessary for them, that having tinnitus is preventing them from hearing something that they do not wish to hear; that being overweight is protecting them from something else. What ever the problem, their sub-conscious believes that they have a need for it and will naturally put up a resistance to the symptoms being taken away because it will leave them without the protection that their computer believes they need. One of the most effective ways of putting up resistance is to increase the symptoms and there is a percentage of cases where this will happen.

This may even happen to people who have responded well to getting rid of certain problems. One lady comes to my mind who presented me with three problems at the consultation. She was a very bad nail biter, she suffered a lot of tension and also had bad arthritis in her hands, feet, wrists, hips and knees. A psychotherapist had given her six sessions of hypnosis and stopped her biting her nails for approximately two months and I asked her if he had made any attempt to find out why she was biting her nails, which anybody using hypnosis in any way professionally should have done. She replied that he had given her identical treatment on each occasion that she had visited him and ended up by recording the last session on a tape for her to take away. If ever there was a case of a man taking money under false pretences this appeared to be it, because if he did identical treatments on each occasion, then he could have recorded the first session with the lady and not persuaded her to come back for further treatments. It took us three treatments to find out why she was biting her nails, and correct that. It took just a further one treatment to find out and correct the cause of her very considerable tension and a further two sessions to find out that the reason for her arthritis was that she did a full time job at work, did a tremendous amount of work at home and when her husband said, "Joan, we'd be better off without you," she developed her arthritis so that she had a good excuse not to work at home, to show him how life would be for him if he had to do everything for himself. Later, she and her husband were divorced and she has since remarried and is very happy. She certainly no longer has any need for her arthritis and things are steadily improving all the time, though of course, it does take time for the body to renew and repair damage once it is done.

A little while after we had finished treating these problems for this patient, she came back saying her husband had suggested that we correct her fear of water. She told me that she knew how to swim but was too frightened to do so. As Joan had reacted so well to the previous treatment and got rid of all those other problems, in far less time than I had suggested to her would be necessary, we both thought we would have no trouble finding out why she had this fear of water. Both of us were very wrong. We went back to the age of twenty in the swimming baths. Her husband was swimming up and down continually under water as she watched. Time and time again we got that information from her. We knew it was the true incident but we had difficulty in seeing the details. In fact, she would not see anything else at all and I reverted then to the method of questioning which gives a yes/no answer, without the patient having to see anything whatsoever. The question and answer process went as follows:

"Is your fear of water due to a fear of difficulty in breathing?"

"No".

"Has your fear been caused by something your husband said?"

"Yes"

"Has it also been caused by something that he did?"

"Yes."

"Is the thing that he said more important to this fear than what he did?"

"No."

"So what he did had a greater effect in creating this fear than what he said?"

"Yes."

"Is the fear, a fear of physical damage?"

"Yes."

"Is it fear of physical damage to you?"

"Yes."

"Would that physical damage happen when you were in the water?"

"Yes."

"Was the physical damage such that you would expect pain?"

"No."

"Would you expect to bleed from this damage?"

"No."

"Would you expect broken bones from this damage".

"No."

"Could this damage be caused anywhere except in water?"

"No."

"Is it anything to do with the fear of drowning, is it the unpleasant sensation of breathing in water?"

"No."

"Is it the fear of water getting into your lungs?"

"No."

I then changed tactics a little:

"Is it the fear or embarrassment of people watching you while you are swimming?"

"No."

"Is it fear of your swimming costume coming off while you're swimming or getting out of the water?"

"No."

"Is it actual fear of physical damage to you that lies at the root of your problem?"

"Yes".

"Would this damage be done to you above the waist?"

"Yes."

"Would this damage be done to you below the waist?"

"Yes."

"Would it be internal damage?"

"No."

"Would it be external damage?"

"Yes."

"Would it be damage to your skin?"

"No."

"Would it be damage to your muscles?"

"Yes."

"Did your husband get cramp while he was swimming?"

"No."

"Have you experienced cramp while swimming?"

"No."

"Is it the fear of cramp that is causing the problem?"

"No."

At the time of writing this chapter, I am still working with Joan. We have had four sessions together so far on her water problem and while we are still working together, we cannot consider her or myself as a failure. She is proving to be a real tough-nut which is surprising in view of the speed at which we sorted out the major problems with which she had come. At the moment I feel that I am going round in ever decreasing circles with her and she might end up as a failure as regards her confidence in her swimming although I know, as she does, that she is a vastly different woman, her arthritis is easing, her tension has completely gone and she has no inclination at all to put her fingers near her mouth to bite her nails. We may win with her and we could win at the very next session but her sub-conscious is fighting hard to hold on to her fear. Could it believe it is saving her from drowning but is not prepared to envisage the possibility and admit it to me?

Every now and then people will experience an increase in their symptoms while having treatment. While we are trying to bring back the memory the sub-conscious will put up a resistance. Thus, a person with a blushing problem could find that they blush more easily and for less reason once we start getting near to the cause of their problem. The occasional person with a weight problem whose weight may have been stationary for the last three or four years will actually put on weight as a means of resistance. None of this is important because the stronger the resistance the nearer to the cause we are getting and once the cause is re-interpreted the symptoms will automatically disappear. It is unfortunate that some people do not expect this symptom increase and that when they realise that they are getting worse they may cease treatment not believing that this is the sign that we are actually near solving the problem for them.

This increase in symptoms is rare and to suffer them for a couple of weeks is a small price to pay for a permanent cure. Their problem will only get worse for a short period and only when we are near the end of the treatment - when we are near the cause of their complaint is the time when resistance could possibly become greater.

One lady who came to lose weight was most certainly a failure. I am still puzzling over why. She was unable (or unwilling) to visualize anything at all and we had to rely entirely on the 'yes/no' method of questioning. We went back to the age of sixteen and she was in the park with several friends, boys and girls. She had no special feeling for any of them but apparently she made a fool of one of the boys and this caused a feeling of anger against herself.

On three occasions we went back to this same incident trying to find out more, but she refused to give me any other information. So I started on a different trail of questioning, with the blunt question:

"Is that incident the true incident which has caused you to become overweight?" and I got the answer "No."

"Did the true incident take place before you were sixteen?"

"No."

"Did the true incident take place after you were sixteen?"

"No."

"Did the true incident take place when you were sixteen?"

"No."

"Are you prepared to indicate to me the true incident which has caused you to become overweight?"

"No."

"Now Maureen, we are dealing with a very logical part of your mind. Is there a logical reason why you are not prepared to indicate the true incident to me?"

"No."

"So, in that case, will you indicate the true incident to me?"

"No."

"Now, you've come here for my help to lose weight isn't that so?"

"Yes".

"So will you tell me the true incident that has caused you to become overweight?"

"No."

"But you are going to be a happier, more energetic, more attractive, more relaxed person when you lose weight, aren't you?"

"No."

"Are you telling me that you are not going to be happier when you lose weight?"

"Yes."

"But you have come here to actually lose weight. Do you feel that you are going to be put in some sort of temptation if you lose weight?"

"No."

"Do you feel that your excess weight is a punishment?"

"Yes."

"You have been overweight for about thirty years which is a longer period of punishment than somebody gets for committing murder. Was the crime you committed worse than murder?"

"No."

"So you've done, already a longer sentence than a murderer. Surely there is no reason now to go on punishing yourself, is there?"

"No."

"Is it time your punishment ended?"

"Yes."

"We can end your punishment when you see the incident that is causing you to be overweight, to over-eat, and you know we can because there is an incident there, isn't there?"

"Yes."

"And you know we can correct it don't you?"

"Yes."

"So will you tell me what that incident was and end your life-sentence?"

"No."

"Is there any reason why you shouldn't tell me?"

"No."

"If there is no reason and you want to lose weight, then you will tell me won't you?"

"Yes."

"So will you tell me?"

"No."

Round and round in circles we went with this lady, I ended up by reserving four times the normal length of treatment time, free of charge, for this lady to try to break through. For some reason I failed and during treatment on this occasion, she continually came out of hypnosis as soon as I started pushing for the truth about the incident that caused her to become overweight. She sat up in her chair fully alert and very apologetic. This happened about four times, presumably because on this occasion she knew that I had reserved all the additional time before hand, with the intention of finding out. There was no way that her sub-conscious wanted me to uncover what her mind had hidden.

Luckily, people like this are very rare indeed. Out of the hundreds that cross my threshold every year, there are three or four who, for one reason or another, are failures. Whether that fault lies with them or with me is in my opinion unimportant. The fact that they are not cured is the only important point. Virtually everyone who has the patience to come the very few times that are necessary, end up disposing of their problem - and disposing of it for ever. Maybe it is because failures are so few that I feel each one so deeply.

There are, of course, the other failures: the people who come and put a fence around themselves. Those who give you certain boundaries, like the elderly lady who, at the consultation insisted that if it was anything to do with her youth she did not want to remember anything at all about her family. When I found out that the incident that lay at the root of her trouble had occurred in her youth, I had to bring her out of hypnosis and tell her that the decision was hers. Either she had to go back and see or she had to live with the terrible pain that she was suffering. Amazingly enough, she decided to live with the pain and ceased treatment. I tried to explain to her that seeing would cure her and that there was no way that telling me what had happened would cause her any embarrassment or guilt, that she would never have to look me in the face again when she had finished treatment. I tried gentle persuasion. I tried argument. I tried logic. I tried emotion. Nothing would shift her; she was adamant and is therefore still suffering. I ended up trying simple symptom removal but the 'need' for her symptom was too great and she could not accept alleviation of her pain.

Was the failure hers or mine? Was there some way I could have got her to accept?

Dear David,

I would like to thank you for helping me to stop biting my nails. I have had the habit for years and tried all the usual remedies but nothing helped me until I came to you. Now for the first time in my life i've got lovely long nails and have no desire to bite them ever again.

I also want to thank you for three other problems you've helped me with

– – – – – – – – –

helped me with my fear of water, I can cope with that now. The third problem

Female Age 48

Travel Panic

The first time that James went into hypnosis he was obviously beautifully relaxed until just before the end of the first session when I said to him:

"I told you before I relaxed you that the whole secret of success in this treatment is acceptance by you, and the way you have so readily accepted hypnosis this afternoon means that we are going to be able to find out the cause of your problem and put it right without difficulty. Within a very few weeks you will have lost this terrible feeling of panic for ever."

The moment I used the words 'get rid of your panic', his breathing rate increased very rapidly and within a few seconds he came straight out of hypnosis, fully alert once more. I told him not to worry that for some reason or other he needed that panic to save him from something worse and the moment I said we would get rid of it his subconscious mind reacted by making him panic, to stop me from giving him treatment. Although his conscious mind wanted to get rid of it, which is why he had come for treatment, his subconscious mind knew that, for some reason or other the panic was very necessary to him.

His main problem was travelling. Anytime he went on a bus, a train or in a car, whether as a passenger or driver, he believed that he was going to be ill and this caused his terrible feeling of panic within him. The next time he came for treatment I relaxed him once more. I started off by pointing out that the feeling of panic was an incorrect reaction which could only be caused by wrong information in that computer-like part of the brain. I then started to go through the processes of finding out what caused this feeling of panic. He had already told me that four years ago he was taken ill on a bus and the driver had suggested dropping him off at the hospital. That was his first illness on transport and his panic dated from that. But although that was what triggered it off, I had to find out what caused him to react to that illness in that way. There was something previous to that which caused him this unnatural feeling.

At first he visualised bandages, there was something bandaged, it could be him but he was not sure. In other words, his subconscious was only allowing him to see that little bit. Then I found that the incident that was causing him problems happened before he was two years old. There was fear, fear of physical damage to him. He was damaged in some sort of an accident and he had received medical treatment. This was as far as we were able to get at the second session but in the next session he visualised himself at his aunt's house, near the stairs, and he saw his aunt fall down them. He also said that he was insecure because he did not know this aunt well. Nor did he know anyone else who was there. Again, as with the last session, to elicit this amount of information had taken all the time available.

At the next session we found that although he had been telling me a bit of truth he had been reinterpreting. It was not his aunt who fell down the stairs, it was himself. He had not wanted to see it at the previous session because it was getting too close to the actual thing which was causing his panic. However, at the following session, it turned out that his own fall down the stairs had needed medical attention; also the stairs were at his own house, not his aunt's. I took him forward a little bit more. There were doctors; they were putting metal things in his mouth, they were forcing him to open his mouth. He was in hospital. There was an anaesthetic. He was frightened of anaesthetic. There were gas and lights. Everything was white. He was awake once more in a ward. The nurses did not like him. They took his cakes, his sweets and his fruit and they made him eat the food that he did not want to. The food that he liked they gave away to the other people in the ward. There was no-one there that he knew. There were no toys, he was lonely and insecure. There was no-one to talk to and no-one wanted to talk to him. He was a long, long time in hospital - three or four days. He had this terrible fear of being put to sleep. There was a feeling of terrible loneliness and hostility towards him.

It was difficult to get information out of James, but when we got this far, both he and I knew that we were onto the real problem. He confirmed that he had been 'badly treated' in hospital. His teeth had been extracted. He connected hospitals with loneliness and hostility and that one incident on the bus when he felt ill had caused him to react to transport with panic in case he was taken ill on a bus again and ended up in hospital. So we went back once more through the actual events at the hospital and eventually, after considerable difficulty he agreed that the nurse had not, in reality, been hostile, that taking food away from him may have been their standard practice, depending on the sort of treatment that he was likely to receive. He had been very young, could not understand any of this. All he knew was they had taken away his food, but he accepted that there no hostility. At the end of this session we had got rid of his hostility with regard to hospitals, but he still had a fear of being anaesthetized.

The next time he came for treatment, we went back again and we worked on this fear of the anaesthetic. His sub-conscious was extremely stubborn. Eventually, we managed to overcome this and using the "yes/no" method of questioning, I re-checked;

"Have we now got rid of your fear of anaesthetics, of being anaesthetized?"

"Yes."

"Have you got rid of the fear of hostility, from staff or patients, doctors or nurses, in hospital?"

"Yes."

"Were these at the root of your panic?"

"Yes."

"So, as you have got rid of them now, have you now lost this feeling of panic?"

"No."

"Is there something else associated with that incident which is still causing panic?"

"Yes."

"Was it the metal things they put in your mouth?"

"Yes."

"But you had damaged yourself hadn't you?"

"Yes."

"And you needed treatment didn't you?"

"Yes."

"So those people were helping you to get rid of that pain, to get rid of that damage?"

"Yes."

"So, if they were working for your good, you should not have any feeling of panic associated with that, should you?"

"No."

"Therefore, isn't it logical - and your sub-conscious is very logical - isn't it logical to lose that feeling of panic?"

"Yes."

"Can you therefore lose that feeling of panic now?"

"No."

Once again, his sub-conscious was being stubborn. This obviously was no reflection on him. It was just the belief of the sub-conscious that he needed that panic. It did not want him in any situation where he may end up in the hands of the doctors. The following time he came, he said he knew the hostility had gone and that his fear of anaesthetics had disappeared, but he still got knots in his stomach when he thought about going into hospital. Under hypnosis once more we found out that his feeling stemmed from when things were put into his mouth at the hospital. They had held him down, they had given him no explanation of what they were going to do. They had put all sorts of metal things in his mouth and he was absolutely scared. I knew we were reaching the end of the road with him. I knew that, although his panic was still as strong as it had been when he first came into the Hypnotherapy Centre, we were very near to cracking his problem once and for all.

"This happened when you were very young didn't it?"

"Yes."

"You were too young to have understood any of the explanations given to you, weren't you?"

"Yes."

"Is it possible that instead of being forcibly held down, a nurse just put a hand on your shoulder to try and comfort you or held your head to keep it steady for the doctor or dentist? Is that a possibility?"

"Yes."

"But you were very, very young. You had had no experiences like this before and you were too young to have an explanation given to you. You could very easily have interpreted that comforting, steadying hand as being forcibly restraining."

"Yes."

"Because you had never had a similar experience, and because you were already in an upset frame of mind from the pain you were suffering, isn't it more than likely that you misinterpreted those hands in that way?"

"Yes."

"So are you now able to put that into perspective, and accept it for the truth and to lose that feeling of panic?"

"No."

"But you do accept that the likelihood of being forcibly restrained is very, very slight?"

"Yes."

"So is it the things they were putting into your mouth that is still causing the problem?"

"Yes."

"Yet you know what they were doing for you was done for your good, to ease your pain and discomfort?"

"Yes."

"Was it because they didn't give you an explanation?"

"Yes."

"That happened when you were very, very young. You are now an adult (he was thirty-three years old) and as an adult, you would not only be given an explanation, but you could demand an explanation. You would have to give permission for anything like that to be done. At the age when this incident actually happened, your permission wasn't needed and in fact you could not have understood enough to give that permission, but now you can. Now you have that control, you can now lose the feeling of panic regarding hospitals, can't you?"

"No."

"Yet you do accept, don't you, that no-one can do anything to you now without giving you full explanations, without describing to you what they are going to do?"

"Yes."

"And you still can't lose your panic?"

"No."

"Is this purely and simply because they didn't tell you, they didn't give you an explanation?"

"Yes."

"But they will give you an explanation now won't they?"

"Yes."

"Do you believe that they will give you the truth now?"

"No."

"Do you believe they will actually lie to you?"

"Yes."

"Now let's face facts, James. A doctor may possibly skim over some of the truth when it comes to what is actually wrong with someone. Particulary if they are seriously ill and the doctor thinks that telling them about that illness may be detrimental to them: but they can't actually lie to them about what they are going to do, they can't tell them they are going to do one thing and immediately turn round and do something completely different because no adult patient would accept it. An adult patient has to give permission for anything like this to be done to them, and you would have to give permission in a similar situation now, wouldn't you?"

"Yes."

"And even on that occasion they didn't actually lie to you about what they were going to do, did they?"

"No."

"Even though you were, then, only a very young child?"

"Yes."

"The doctor, before he does anything to you, has to tell you roughly what it is that he is going to do. Otherwise, the moment he starts to do something different an adult is going to object."
He started to talk then:

"If I object they will refuse to give me treatment."

"But James, you are still looking at this with they eyes of a young child" I told him, "A doctor knows that if he tells you he is going to do something , and then does something completely different, which is going to be obvious to you, he knows you are going to object. And if you did object he wouldn't refuse to treat you, he would have to tell you the truth. Any adult would object to a treatment different to that explained to them by a doctor and if doctors then refused to treat them, everybody would be walking around untreated and doctors would be made redundant, Every adult has the right to know what is going to be done to their bodies, and every doctor has a legal and moral responsibility to do only what they tell the patient they are going to do."

Gradually, bit by bit, I wore him down. The whole episode at the hospital must have been a complete nightmare to James. Far worse than the actual falling downstairs and damaging his teeth. That was a very minor incident. The examination with him being held down and having things put in his mouth, then the actual anaesthetic and imagined hostility, taking the food off him, nobody talking to him. All this had been a horrifying experience to him.

But the last time he came for treatment he was fine. The panic had gone and to prove to himself that it had completely gone he had spent the whole of one day riding around the City of Birmingham on buses. He said he had started off with some trepidation, wondering whether it had really worked and, on the first couple of rides, that query caused him some slight feelings of panic. As the day wore on and he took the fourth or fifth ride, he was happy, he was at ease, and he knew with one hundred percent certainty that his fear of hospitals and everything else connected with them had completely disappeared. He knew that the chances of being taken ill on a bus and ending in a hospital were very slim, and that even if it did happen he could still accept it without any unnatural reaction whatsoever. He had never had any worries about being ill at home as there he felt he could always recover without recourse to hospital treatment. He had no real illness in his life - the worst he had ever felt was during that bus ride when the driver had suggested he go to hospital.

Dear DAVID

Just a Few Lines on thanking you for your Help on gaining my confidence as before I come to you I used to Blush a LOT at work But now I am completely confiden and can talk a LOT more at work to people.

So if this Letter is PRINTED I would Like to Say to anyBody who

Does Blush Like i did all the time. then Get help it can Be cured as I no it can Be.

Thanks DAVID

Male Age 16

To David happy christmass

Thanks for everything at least I have had my real presents even if you didnt give me it at christmass

Male Age 21

Forgotten Memories

Whether or not every single thing that happens is permanently recorded in the memory banks of our personal computer can never be ascertained with complete certainty, but my belief is that everything that ever happened, every word that we have ever heard, is stored in our minds.

Certainly, anything that affects us in any way at all has the information tucked away somewhere. It is only a matter of finding out what it is. Sometimes people with problems have difficulty in recalling the particular memories that cause the problems, but this is not a question of the memory not being there. This may be a question of the sub-conscious mind not wishing to bring back the memory into the conscious mind because of the unwelcome emotions that were caused at the time or because the conscious mind when in its normal state, fully alert, and not under hypnosis, cannot recall memories that the person wishes to bring back because when that memory has not been used for a long time, it gets overlaid with other things and gradually buried too deep for the person to recall themselves. Thus, one occasionally gets the person who comes with the specific request to be able to recall a certain piece of information.

One lady who came in a considerable state of tension because she and her husband were about to move into a new house the following week, and she had suddenly remembered that somewhere she had hidden some letters from a lover whom she had some years back. She was really worried. She knew that she had hidden them but she could not remember where. She was worried that her husband may come across them in the move. Could I help her to find them? To recall where they were?

Under hypnosis we went back to the day when she had decided to hide them. She was in her bedroom standing with the letters in her hand, looking around the room, wondering where to put them. Eventually she moved the dressing table a little, pulled up the carpet and put the letters under the carpet before replacing the dressing table.

She was a good example of a person only accepting under hypnosis what they want to accept and having the ability to come out of hypnosis whenever they wish, because as soon as she had seen the event and told me about it, she came straight out of hypnosis without any prompting from me, with a smile on her face and a sigh of relief. She thanked me for my help. I was pleased with the quick result and was tempted to let her go but I felt, as I always do with anybody who has a problem, that it must be checked, and double checked, and then checked again. She said it was not necessary, I said that I considered it was and that she should allow me to do so. It was just as well that I had insisted because back under hypnosis once more, I checked that they were still there, in the same place and I got the answer "No." So we went through the process once more, and this time we found that she had taken the letters from under the carpet and put them in the book on the top shelf of the wardrobe in her bedroom. This time she stayed in the same relaxed state to give me a chance to check and two or three hours later she telephoned me to say that she had recovered them safely and had already burnt them in the back garden.

I imagined her feelings had she gone home without having the check made, believing that those letters were under the carpet. Going into her bedroom, moving the dressing table, pulling up the carpet and finding the letters gone. Her automatic assumption would have been that her husband had found them and this would obviously have caused a lot of anguish. One gets many patients who feel better when a therapist knows that they are only half way through a treatment. I never feel happy until I am able to say to someone, "The treatment is completed." If they stop before then, I have doubts about the permanent success just as in this case of a forgotten memory.

One gets all sorts of requests to uncover lost items, like a valuable diamond ring which a lady had pushed down into a jar of face cream for safe keeping and then, not being keen on that particular face cream, had put it away in a drawer and forgotten about it. She had forgotten about the cream and in doing so had forgotten about the ring. The lady who put some gold bracelets in the boot of her car under the spare wheel and was worried about recovering one of them in particular because it had been a present from her husband who had mentioned that he had not seen her wear it for a long time. Or the Asian girl in her early twenties who had lost contact with her family and wanted to recall the details of her father's passport in the hope that this would help her contact her family. I had taken her back to the last time that she had seen the inside page of her father's passport, and I sat with my pen poised over a piece of paper and asked her to tell me the details on that page so I could write them down, but suddenly realised that, although the girl's English was very near perfect, her father may not have had a British passport and it may have been made out in Punjabi or Urdu, so I had to instruct her to wake up with the precise picture of the passport right in the forefront of her mind, with every word clear and then give her the paper to write it down.

Many people have the mistaken belief that if one is treating a person whose original language is different from that being used under treatment and the patient is taken back to before they had any knowledge of the therapist's language, the therapist can lose contact with the patient. In other words, assume I am using English and treating someone who comes from China, who did not know any English until the age of fifteen. If we find that the problem was caused at the age of ten and take them back to five years before they had any knowledge of English, will they still be able to respond to my words which are in a language that they did not understand at that age? The short answer to this is that they will. By taking them back to a memory before they had a knowledge of English does not wipe out all subsequent knowledge. They are seeing things in their mind just as we all see things throughout every day of our lives when we recall memories. If you are watching a film on the television you can use your imagination to feel sad. The film may bring a tear to your eye or a lump to your throat or in an exiting situation you may feel tension. In a really good film you can actually feel your heart beat increase, because you are using your imagination and even if you are sitting at home reading a good book, a book that really grips you, you can feel the tension rising within yourself, within your body. You are translating the cold print on the page in your imagination into a type of reality. Then you are physically responding to the reality that you create but all the time that you are using your imagination in this way you are still as conscious as you wish to be to your surroundings. You cannot lose yourself in that imagination any more than one can under hypnosis. Seeing old events under hypnosis does not wipe out subsequent knowledge. One lies there, imagining, pulling up a memory from the past, just as one may do when one is talking to a friend, but still being aware of the time and place and knowing that one is only relaxed and remembering.

There are, of course, situations where one wants to forget and where it serves no purpose to bring back memories. Most people know of amnesia following an accident and reviving memories like this is normally a useless operation, they are best left forgotten. Occasionally it may be worthwhile recovering the memory up to the point of the accident to find out how it was caused but to bring back the memory of the actual accident itself normally serves no useful purpose. The most useful purpose is served by the protective part of the mind, in the forgetting.

On the other hand, one occasionally gets people who come because they wish to forget, and in certain circumstances this sort of thing can be advantageous. The lady who came having attempted suicide because she believed that she had killed her husband asked me to wipe out all memories of her husband, but was asking the impossible. She not only had children who would have been a constant reminder that she used to have a man in her life, but she was also receiving regular monthly payments from an insurance company as a result of the death of her husband. There were so many things in her life that would have gone on reminding her, that to try to wipe out all memory of her husband would have been impossible quite apart from the fact that it would have served no purpose. What we needed to do was to find out why she reacted to the death of her husband with this terrible guilt and put that right. She would then accept his death, keep the happy memories that she had of her marriage, and lose the terrible feeling that had caused her to attempt suicide, which was the final straw that made her son bring her to me all the way from the south coast for treatment.

This lady knew that she was guilty and that guilt was the source of her problem. I asked her how she had killed her husband, and she told me that when the doctor had told her husband that he needed an operation on his prostate, he had said that the waiting list on the national health was about eighteen months, but if he wanted the operation quicker he could pay for it privately, and it could be done almost immediately. My patient said to the doctor that having paid all these years into the health insurance scheme, it seemed a shame that she should have to pay extra for the operation. She had sufficient money to pay but she thought it was wrong that she should have to. She did not actually refuse to pay but the doctor obviously got the impression that she did not want to pay and so the husband was put on the waiting list for a Health Service operation. During this operation there was, according to this lady, an error which caused her husband's death. She believed that an error like this could not have been made if she had agreed to pay for her husband's operation. It was by refusing to pay privately that she killed her husband.

She told me this at the consultation before using hypnosis and went on to say that she had brought up her children wrongly. One son of sixteen did nothing all day but sit in his bedroom listening to records and this was because she had not brought him up correctly. Here again she was at fault, she was guilty. There were other incidents where things were not perfect and where she took all the blame on herself because she obviously had the belief that she was a guilty type.

Under hypnosis, we uncovered the original reason, the original guilt. When she was thirteen she lived on a farm in Ireland with a large number of brothers and sisters. She was the youngest and they had no time to spare for her; her mother was always too busy and her older brothers and sisters were always working. The only person who was able to spare her any time was her father, who was a bed-ridden invalid and she could not spend all her time with him so she became friendly with some of the local lads. To keep their friendship at the age of thirteen she started having sexual intercourse with them. Later on she brought this out in confession to her priest and he literally 'gave her hell', because that is what she suffered for the rest of her life. He used the word 'guilt'. He told her that she must stop. He told her that she would be damned in the eyes of God and she left that confessional where she had gone for comfort and to ease herself, feeling more rejected that she had before. The only people she could turn to for comfort were the same lads that she had been having intercourse with. So she went back to having sex with them, but every time she did she knew that she was guilty, she knew that God was piling up more and more punishment for her, and step by step as we went through her life under hypnosis, the sorry picture emerged.

When things happened that a normal person would consider as unfortunate, she considered herself as guilty. There was no such thing as bad luck in her life, no such thing as other people responding wrongly. All these things were her fault, because of her guilt. Right up to her son playing records instead of being out enjoying himself (no thought that music was his method of enjoying himself, and a not uncommon method in this day of pop music on tape and discs), and from there to when her husband died - even that was her fault. We corrected the feeling of guilt caused by sex in her early teens and gradually altered the reactions to every other event in her life, which had been based on that first guilt. By the end of the treatment she had accepted that she was not to blame for her husband's death, nor for all the other events that led up to her attempted suicide, and was able to look back on her married life with pleasure, with regret for the loss of her husband, but no guilt.

DUDLEY W. MID.

Dear Mr Lesser. 11. 10 83

In the past few weeks I have met two people who have been patients of yours, and both were pleased with the results, one a migraine sufferer. the other had a storm phobia, which brings me to a problem of my own. I have an absolutely, diabolical, memory, try as I might the most important things just dissapear

Male Age 37

my confidence has been thus restored that

Female Age 53

Sex is Dirty

I opened the door myself when the bell rang. I expected to see a lady as I had a Mrs Phillips down for a consultation in my appointment book. The man who was standing on the other side of the door said, "Mrs Phillips". I tried not to look surprised and as he walked in he was followed by a lady who been hiding behind him. That was Mrs Phillips. They came into my consulting room and made themselves comfortable, or at least Mr Phillips made himself reasonably comfortable. Mrs Phillips was obviously very, very embarrassed indeed, so I asked them straight away, to get the embarrassment behind us all, what the problem was, and Mr Phillips said that his wife could not relax.

The embarassment in the air was so thick that I thought we would never get anywhere unless I cut through it, so I said, "Do you mean sexually?"

The answer was yes.

Mrs Phillips was more than embarrassed, she was terrified. Apparently she had read about sex-therapists and was expecting to be physically examined and physically tested for her sexual responses. I talked to them both and told them that there was no such fear, that it was something in her mind that was stopping her enjoying sex. All we had to do was find out what it was and put it right so that we could get rid of her problem. She appeared still as apprehensive because she still felt that even talking about sex or her own reactions was just too embarrassing. However, she wanted to become normal, and finally we started treatment although the effort and the fear on her part was very obvious indeed.

Apparently she had, at one time enjoyed sex, at least to some extent, but her husband said that she had really had the problem since before she left school. They told me at the consultation that when she was fourteen she had a baby, who now lived with her mother. They also told me that prior to getting pregnant she had been raped. She had been married for nine years and was now twenty eight years old.

I deliberately kept my explanations of hypnosis and what it felt like very short because it was obvious that Mrs Phillips could not really believe what I was saying to her. The only way to overcome her fear was to get her to experience hypnosis. So I relaxed her. I took her into a very pleasant state of relaxation, into a good state of hypnosis, and pointed out to her that although she was in hypnosis she was still in control. There was no possible way that I could give her instructions or force her to answer any questions. She was the one who was in control and was using her control to follow my words which had made her become very, very relaxed. Afterwards, when she stood up to leave the room, her words were, "that wasn't as bad as I had expected." So I told her that next time she came, we would actually start to find out what was at the root of her problem, but she would only be in the same state as she had been today; she would still have control. Some days later when she came back, she was a little more relaxed than she had been the first time she had crossed the threshold, but still apprehensive.

On this occasion, after relaxing her, she took me back to the age of twenty five, when she had been in hospital for a sterilization operation. She did not want to be sterilized as she wanted more than the three children they had at the moment, but the doctor said that she should not have any more children. She felt less of a woman than before she had been sterilized. We talked around this event for some time. I was trying to get her to go back further because, obviously, whatever was causing the problem had occurred long before she was twenty five. Eventually she went back to fourteen when she had been raped in her own home by a friend. She was quite adamant that she had not led him on, that what had happened was completely unexpected to her. The experiencee was uncomfortable for her and she had got no pleasure at all. I asked her if that was the first time she had had intercourse. She told me that she had had it once before, again without experiencing pleasure, only discomfort. I then asked her if she was pregnant from the first time she had intercourse or from the time she was raped. The answer was no, it was the third time she had intercourse from which she became pregnant. On further questioning, it turned out that the boy she had intercourse with the first time, the one that raped her and the one that got her pregnant, were all the same person. I began to doubt the story of rape. I felt there was a good chance that she had built up in her mind the belief that she had been raped, but I said nothing about this to her, and it was not until the next session that the truth came out.

She had encouraged him, she had led him on by words, and she was feeling guilty about it, but it appeared that a more strong emotion was the feeling she had let herself be used. She also had a feeling of rejection from her parents. Her guilt was mainly towards them. It appeared that what she was considering as rape was not rape. She had wanted intercourse and she had wanted enjoyment, but instead of enjoyment, she had experienceed pain, and she mixed pain with her guilt and translated it into rape. It was not rape as both partners wanted sex. However, to call it rape lessened her feelings of guilt towards her parents, particularly after she got pregnant the next time they had intercourse. She felt as though she had let her parents down, that she was naughty, that it should not have happened. There was also a feeling of guilt towards her child because she does not appear to feel that the child gets the love from its grandparents that she should be giving it - and that the child knows it. She felt cheap, mainly because of the words used by her mother when she got pregnant. Her mother's attitude, even before she got pregnant, was that people who enjoyed sex are cheap, and when she got pregnant and her mother became aware of the fact that she was having sex, she started to feel cheap. Her mother called her a fool, said that she had let her down, that she had let herself down, she had made herself cheap and she was very disgusted with her. As she loves her mother, she felt very guilty towards her. Once again we came to the end of the session, and she left saying that the treatment was obviously going to be far less distasteful to her than she had ever imagined possible.

The next time we were really able to make progress because, although she was continually talking about the period when she was fourteen years old, I knew that was not the true root of the problem. The first time she had intercourse she was willing yet she had no pleasurable sensations whatsoever. There had to be a reason for that, there had to be something previous to that first session of intercourse which caused her unnatural reactions at the time.

At this session she went back to the age of eight. Three boys and two girls were with her out in the country, all around about eight years old. Not the age one would think of for experts in the sexual field! They were talking about sex and one of the boys said that it was only for the man's enjoyment, another one disagreed and said that it was dirty for everyone and that a normal man did not even enjoy it. The two girls were arguing with them. They said the boys were telling lies. They said that sex was pleasurable, otherwise why should nearly every adult do it? They apparently discussed this between themselves for quite a long time.

She took no part in the discussion, neither did one of the boys, and when the subject was changed she ended up with the same belief as the boys. She knew that getting involved in sex was dirty, she knew that it was not supposed to be enjoyed. Her mother's words that people who enjoy sex were cheap, and the other expressions used by her mother reinforced it. So the first time she had intercourse she could not enjoy it and this reinforced the belief even further. The second time she had intercourse her muscles had been so tense that she had actually experienced pain and she called it rape. That pain had added to the belief that sex was not supposed to be enjoyed and, therefore, anyone who enjoyed it was abnormal and dirty.

She had one more appointment with me, and she came in with a big smile on her face. She had not actually 'made it', she had not actually experienced an orgasm, but during that week they had sex three times and each time she had gone higher in feelings that the time before. She knew that within the next couple of times she would experience a full orgasm. She knew it. There was no doubt whatsoever in her mind; there was no guilt, there was no feeling of being dirty. She looked back on the old words that she had heard and realized that kids of eight knew nothing of sex, cannot know anything about sexual feelings, that they were talking without any knowledge whatsoever. Yet she had taken their words and reinforced them with the words of her mother. These were in her sub-conscious before she came into contact with people who enjoyed sex and she went into sex for the first time 'knowing' that anyone who enjoyed it was not normal, and there was no way that she was going to allow herself to enjoy it.

We parted company with her saying that she had been silly to be so apprehensive and shy at the beginning, but of course her whole attitude to sex, to talking about sex, to her actual sexual feelings within herself, had changed. Now she is normal, now she is happy, and what is just as important, her husband feels adequate because he can get her to achieve full sexual satisfaction. He himself feels more of a man and no longer feels that he is just using her. He is giving as much as he gets when they indulge.

Bye the way I survived my
week in London without any
Stomach pains (hangovers excluded)!
Thanks again

Female Age 28

Logical Causes - Logical Cures

Problems are caused by a logical progression from the incident lying at the root, up to the symptoms that develop. It is a computer logic, a logic without analysis, without commonsense, and therefore to correct the cause needs, above all, a logical mind. One does not need deep learning to be a good hypnotherapist; you need to have the desire to help people and an ability to use logic.

Each individual's experiences are unique to them and the information in the memory banks of their computer is therefore unique to them and they will develop symptoms in their own individual way. In a response to one particular incident they will refer to similar experiencees in the past, thus no two people will have the same symptoms in response to a particular event. Neither will people have more or less identical symptoms always have a similar event as the root of their problem.

The asthma sufferer in a previous chapter had a logical reason for this problem. His sub-conscious decided that he should never do a similar thing in the future. Throwing stones requires exertion and his asthma stopped him exerting himself in any way at all. Another who, at around the same age, had used some very hurtful words to a playmate which he bitterly regretted afterwards, had developed a stutter. Yet another young man, suffering from asthma, had developed it due to a swimming instructor who told him that he would never make a swimmer, and had developed his symptoms so that he got sympathy instead of derision from his school friends. On more that one occasion I have had patients with stutters which have been caused by teachers making a fool of the child in front of the class. The hesitation in speech from then on gave them time to rethink their answers.

Just as different causes can lead to similar symptoms, so similar causes can lead to completely different symptoms. A woman who does not enjoy sex and passes on this belief to her daughter, may cause that daughter to develop a similar dislike for sex or may cause that daughter to develop anorexia because the girl knows that if she eats well she will grow, she will mature. If she does not mature she will not grow up and will not be expected to have sex.

Most doctors appear to believe that lack of regular periods which often goes hand in hand with anorexia, is caused by lack of nutrition. In fact, just as the loss of desire to eat is, in most cases, a wish not to mature, so is the lack of periods. Sometimes this is a fear of sex, sometimes it is the belief that the person, once an adult, will lose a parent's love. There can be many reasons for anorexia just as there can be for any other problem.

One patient who had been treated by a doctor who 'did hypnosis' had, by direct suggestion, been persuaded to eat but ten years after this treatment, when married and twenty eight years old, she came to me still never having had a period because she did not want to be a fully mature person.

The man who was 'pee shy' due to an incident when he was staying at the house of an aunt who made fun of him when he wet the bed, gradually developed the symptom of being unable to pass water anywhere except in his own toilet, in his own home. He used to go to work each day, and get home in the evening in agony with a full bladder. In spite of the discomfort he had a complete inability to pass water in any toilet other than his own.

In all these cases one finds out the incident then talking to the computer one can, using logic, change the programme.

Very often information comes from a patient under treatment to make one assume that the cause of the problem has been found when, by careful checking, it is discovered that this is not the case. The man who was suffering from anxiety had stolen some fireworks from a shop and, with his friends, was in a cemetery setting them off. He was holding his favorite firework in his hand when it spluttered and sparks went into his friends' pocket setting alight the fireworks there. The other boy ended up in hospital having treatment for burns. To me, there were two possible causes in what he had told me: it could have been the guilt about stealing the fireworks or guilt about what he had done to his friend, but neither of these had affected him in any way at all. His anxiety was due to the fact that he was playing with his favorite firework, he was really enjoying himself when everything turned sour. Since then he felt threatened whenever he was enjoying himself. The better things were, the more chance there was of trouble. He reminded me of a retired man who had developed a stammer and a tremendous decrease in his confidence at the age of seventy five due to an incident that happened when he was only five years old.

It had been a beautiful sunny day. He was singing at the top of his voice as he was walking down the street when, all of a sudden, a 'huge animal' came charging at him. He was petrified. He stood still. The animal knocked him over and went running up the street. It turned out that the animal was only a large dog and that it was not charging at him, but running past him. His interpretation was that when things were going right disaster follows. Whenever things were going right for him he anticipated something unpleasant. He used to run his own business and had the usual problems of any small business man. After he had retired from business, there was very little to go wrong in his life, therefore his lack of confidence and anxiety grew as he was continually expecting some sort of disaster to befall him. When he was working he used to talk confidently to other members on the charity committee on which he served, but when he retired and there was really nothing to go wrong in his life, he expected disaster. He lost his confidence and became unsure of what he was saying. Thus his stammer developed although previously there had never been any sign of a stammer at all.

One young lady took me back to an incident which happened when she was six years old, when she and her younger sister were playing on a steep flight of concrete steps between blocks of flats. They were swinging on the handrail and my patient pushed her sister, who fell from top to bottom of that flight, breaking an arm, a rib and fracturing her leg in two places. I asked her if she liked her sister at the time and got the answer "Yes". I asked her if she still got on well with her sister and again had an answer in the affirmative. I was convinced that guilt lay at the root of her problem but it turned out that I was completely wrong. Her sister had been in hospital following this accident for over half a year and my patient was ignored throughout that time - her injured sister was foremost in her parents' minds. At one stage she used the words, "I'm here, too".

It is very easy to treat what the therapist believes needs treating but the patient knows what is causing his problem and the only way to cure it is to treat the actual cause. There is no case in this book that will be duplicated in any way by any other person. Everybody's problem is caused by a unique set of circumstances which cannot be duplicated.

Thinking over these cases in this chapter, I ask a straight forward question: How can direct suggestion do away with the very logical symptoms that a person has developed as a protection - at least without developing alternative symptoms to protect themselves? There is only one way to treat people with incorrect reactions: one must go back, one must find out the cause and put it right. While there is need for protective mechanism to be there, there will always be some symptom and if somebody, by using hypnosis or any other means, prevents a person from exhibiting one symptom they will produce another to take its place.

that, i cant complain compared to what
i was like when i first came to you
can i.
I also ~~dinelnt~~ didnt feel one bit embaresd
about sex, in fact i felt confident enough
to make first moves but ~~...~~

Male Age 21

Dear David,

Having been housebound for 10 years due to suffering from Agoraphobia I am amazed that I now able to look forward to a holiday at the seaside with my family after only two ~~xxxxxxxxxxxx xxxxxx~~ treatments at your clinic, and I am really grateful to my Doctor for suggesting Hypnotherapy.

Obviously I shall be coming to complete the treatment to get rid of the last of my symptons and ensure they will ~~xxxxxxxxxx~~ never re-appear but felt I had to write to say thanks"for what you have done in so short a time after all these years.

Yours sincerely

Female Age 46

The Last Word

It never fails to amaze me how people who have what they know to be a mental problem - such as depression, tension or anxiety - go to a doctor and take pills which they know can only ease the problem for them, and in many cases will not even achieve this. Obviously, someone reacting to a temporary home problem or a problem at work with a natural amount of tension or anxiety may be helped by a pill, although they would be helped even more by hypnosis - without any side effects. However, the reactions within them, the incorrect reactions to external causes, can never be solved by pills, but only by putting right the cause of the incorrect reaction. It is a shame that so many people have to suffer through ignorance of hypnotherapy, through bad professional advice, through fear of hypnosis itself.

I want to use this last chapter to reinforce comments already made in this book that under hypnosis one is awake, one is aware, one knows everything that is said and because one understands everything that is said one can refuse to accept any suggestions that are made. Patients do not have to answer any questions that they do not wish to answer. They are the ones in control and do not ever give up that control to the therapist. They allow the therapist to carry on, but if there are any words said, any question asked they do not like, they can cease their co-operation.

The state of hypnosis is the state immediately before one goes to sleep, when one is conscious, hearing any noises that may go on but not really bothered about them unless there is something to which they SHOULD react. The fact that some people, even after they have been cured of their problem, still do not believe that they have been hypnotised, is a good indication of the state of hypnosis. These people do not believe that they have been hypnotised because nothing dramatic happened. They expected to be 'taken over', to feel my mind groping around inside theirs, or for everything to become blank. Yet before relaxing them I explain what hypnosis is like and explain that it is a state of relaxation that they go into, sometimes only for a second or two, immediately before they go to sleep. When they say that they did not feel hypnotised, I point out to them that this state, immediately before sleep, is a state that they cannot really explain in words. Certainly nothing dramatic happens because nothing happens at night when they go to bed and drift through this state of hypnosis into the state of sleep. In fact so little happens that they are only aware that they have gone to sleep when they wake up again! Therefore nothing dramatic can happen when they only go part of the way into sleep. It is difficult for them to believe that they will not be taken over, not have unwanted thoughts or feelings put into their mind or be made to do silly tricks. One can only repeat that all the time the patient has the final control. It is up to the patient what he accepts and what he rejects. No hypnotherapist, no matter how clever, can make someone accept an idea or do anything against their will.

In the hands of skilled therapists, hypnosis has the tremendous advantage of being a treatment which has no detrimental side effects. The only possible side effect is that the patient can become more relaxed and calm and be able to think clearly and enjoy life more, but it is important that people considering treatment should go to a genuine hypnotherapist and not to a 'symptom remover' or a person who just attempts to relax them. Unfortunately, there are a larger number of these people advertising than there are of genuine hypnotherapists.

Over the years that I have been in practice, the number of hypnotists advertising themselves as hypnotherapists has grown enormously which is why, a few years ago, I commenced courses of training for genuine hypnotherapists as I felt that the profession was in danger of being swamped by unskilled and ignorant people.

When interviewing people before accepting them on one of my training courses, I look for people with logical minds. This is almost the only requirement for hypnotherapy coupled with the desire to help people, patience with the people who 'do nothing but moan' and an understanding that this is a symptom of their problem. I have accepted for training people who wanted to learn out of interest, people who wanted to understand themselves or others better, particularly if they be marriage guidance counsellors or working with difficult children, but the main emphasis of the courses is towards those who wish to become hypnotherapists as my interest is to the further the cause of genuine hypnotherapy and prevent it from being overrun by the people who have discovered that they can hypnotise others but are ignorant of the therapeutic benefits that can be achieved.

you good luck in the valuable work
you perform. You will also be pleased
to learn I am going from strength to
strength now; your treatment has made
an enormous difference to
my life.

Female age 41

The Author

David Lesser had a varied career before becoming a masseur in 1966. In refining his techniques of relaxation massage and learning how to teach them to others, he became interested by the interaction of mind and body, the way such deep mental effects could be achieved by the purely physical treatment of body massage.

He decided to investigate the opposite effect — that of mind over body which led him into hypnosis, then to hypnotherapy and finally into curative hypnotherapy.

One of his four daughters has, so far, followed him into hypnotherapy and runs a successful practice in Birmingham and David himself devotes over 60 hours a week to hypnotherapy — both treating patients and teaching, with a further 12 hours given to teaching and giving massage.

In addition to massage qualifications with most leading examination bodies he is Chairman of the Curative Hypnotherapy Examination Committee and also the President of the Association of Qualified Curative Hypnotherapists.